COMPLETE
HIGHER PHYSICS
REVISION NOTES

Campbell Robertson

Full revision notes for the new
Scottish Higher Physics course

- ideal for revision and exam preparation
- coverage of the whole of the Higher syllabus
- test questions with answers

...the right choice

Preface

The purpose of this book is to provide concise, yet full revision notes for the new Higher Physics exam. Its approach is to try and give confidence to the learner and no unnecessary material is included. The order of the text follows closely the syllabus as laid down by the Scottish Qualifications Authority, although pupils may find their own school teaches topics in a slightly different order to that given here.

Test questions, ☑ **TQ**s, are spread throughout the text to help reinforce learning points. These mainly refer to the use of equations and fully worked solutions are given in Appendix (iii). It is strongly recommended that students also obtain a copy of Practice Questions for Higher Physics (also published by P&N Publications) which will allow the study of each topic followed by practice at questions graded from easy through to the more difficult exam style questions.

I hope you find this book useful and an aid to all the work you have already done.

Campbell Robertson

CONTENTS

UNIT 1 Mechanics and Properties of Matter

UNIT 2 Electricity and Electronics

UNIT 3 Radiation and Matter

UNIT 1 Mechanics and Properties of Matter

Vectors

Vectors and Scalars

A **scalar** quantity is a quantity which is specified by **magnitude alone**.
A **vector** quantity is a quantity which is specified by **both magnitude and direction**.

Consider the two quantities of mass and force. Mass is measured in kilograms and only has magnitude so is a scalar. Force, however, is a quantity in which the direction of the force is just as important as the size of the force. Hence it is a vector quantity.

The table below shows a list of common vector and scalar quantities.

Scalar quantities	Vector Quantities
Speed	Velocity
Distance	Displacement
Temperature	Acceleration
Mass	Force
Energy	Momentum
Work	Impulse
Time	
Power	

Some scalar quantities have equivalent vector quantities. Velocity is the vector equivalent of speed i.e. a velocity has magnitude in a particular direction while speed has no associated direction. Displacement is the vector equivalent of distance i.e. a displacement has direction whilst distance has not. As a result:

$$\text{speed} = \frac{\text{distance}}{\text{time}} \quad \text{and} \quad \text{velocity} = \frac{\text{displacement}}{\text{time}}$$

> ☑TQ 1   A cat walks a distance of 10 m due east along a wall then turns around and walks back a distance of 4 m. This takes it a total time of 24 s. Find the average speed of the cat and also its average velocity.

Addition of Scalars

Two scalar quantities are added or subtracted just as any numbers in arithmetic providing they have the same units e.g. 10 kg + 5 kg gives a total mass of 15 kg.

Addition of Vectors

To add together vector quantities consideration must be given to the direction of the vectors as well as their magnitude. Vectors can be added by one of two methods—**either** by scale diagram **or** by trigonometry.

Vectors can be represented by lines drawn to scale in the direction of the vector. An arrow represents the direction in which the vector is heading.

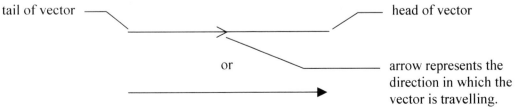

tail of vector   head of vector

or   arrow represents the direction in which the vector is travelling.

Vectors are always added head to tail and a vector sum may consist of two or more vectors. The answer obtained is called the **resultant vector**.

Finding the Resultant using a Scale Drawing
Here are the steps which should be carried out in finding the resultant of a set of vectors. We will use the following example as an illustration.

Example: A bird flies due south at 5 m s⁻¹ and is simultaneously blown east by cross winds at 3 m s⁻¹. Find the resultant velocity of the bird.

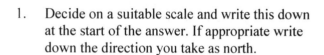

1.   Decide on a suitable scale and write this down at the start of the answer. If appropriate write down the direction you take as north.

   Let 1 cm ⇔ 1 m s⁻¹.

2.   Draw an arrow to represent the first vector ensuring it is the correct size and in the correct direction.

   Let 1 cm ⇔ 1 m s⁻¹.

   velocity of bird of 5 m s⁻¹

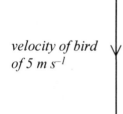

3.   Draw an arrow to represent the second vector starting at the head of the first vector. Vectors are always added head to tail. Continue until all the vectors have been drawn.

   Let 1 cm ⇔ 1 m s⁻¹.

   velocity of bird of 5 m s⁻¹

   cross wind of 3 m s⁻¹

4. The resultant vector is now added by drawing it from the tail of the first vector to the head of the last vector. The resultant vector can be distinguished from other vectors by drawing a double arrow on it. The magnitude and direction of this vector is the required answer. These are found by measuring the line using a ruler and finding the angle with a protractor.

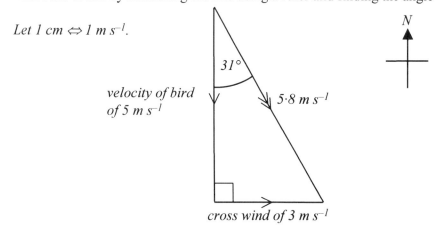

Let 1 cm ⇔ 1 m s⁻¹.

5. When quoting the final answer always ensure you clearly state the magnitude and direction of the resultant.

Bird flies at 5·8 m s⁻¹ at an angle of 31° to the east of south.

It is also possible to quote the direction as a bearing. North is regarded as 000° and the bearing at which our bird is flying would be 149°.

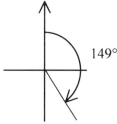

NOTE: If a question asks you to find the resultant using a scale diagram you **must** find the answer by that method and **not** by trigonometry as shown on the next page.

Finding the Resultant using Trigonometry

Providing you are not asked to specifically solve a vector problem by scale drawing you can easily find the answer to a vector problem involving a right angled triangle using Pythagoras' theorem and one of the three trigonometric ratios (sine, cosine and tangent).

Consider the problem involving the bird described previously. Always sketch the situation first so that you know what the approximate answer will be.

The magnitude of the resultant of the two vectors is found by using Pythagoras' theorem.

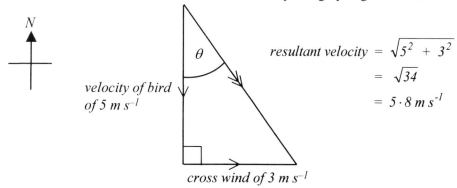

$$resultant\ velocity = \sqrt{5^2 + 3^2}$$
$$= \sqrt{34}$$
$$= 5 \cdot 8\ m\ s^{-1}$$

The direction is found using a trigonometric function i.e.

$$\sin \theta = \frac{opposite}{hypotenuse} \qquad \cos \theta = \frac{adjacent}{hypotenuse} \qquad \tan \theta = \frac{opposite}{adjacent}$$

$$= \frac{3}{5 \cdot 8} \quad \textbf{or} \qquad = \frac{5}{5 \cdot 8} \quad \textbf{or} \qquad = \frac{3}{5}$$

$$= 31° \qquad\qquad = 31° \qquad\qquad = 31°$$

Bird flies at 5·8 m s⁻¹ at an angle of 31° to the east of south.

Finding the Components of a Vector
Two vectors at right angles to one another can be added to produce a resultant vector. It is also possible to take a resultant vector and reduce it to two **rectangular components**.

Suppose an object has a velocity *v* at an angle θ above the horizontal. This vector can be resolved into a horizontal and vertical component by forming a right angled triangle.

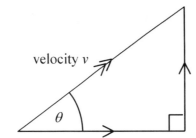

velocity *v*

The vertical component of the velocity *v* can be found by trigonometry so
vertical component $v_\text{v} = v \sin \theta$

θ

The horizontal component of the velocity *v* is also found by trigonometry so
horizontal component $v_\text{h} = v \cos \theta$

The vector components can be redrawn as shown below.

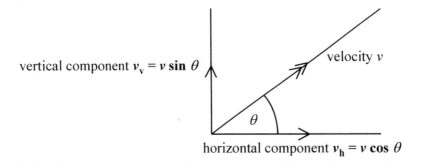

vertical component $v_\text{v} = v \sin \theta$

velocity *v*

θ

horizontal component $v_\text{h} = v \cos \theta$

The technique of splitting a vector into its components will be used later in this section in solving projectile problems.

Equations of Motion

Measuring Acceleration
You will recall from Standard Grade Physics that acceleration can be defined as the rate of change of velocity i.e.

$$\text{acceleration} = \frac{\text{final velocity - initial velocity}}{\text{time}} \qquad a = \frac{v - u}{t}$$

To measure acceleration experimentally it is necessary to measure the initial and final velocity of the object being considered and the time it takes to make any change in velocity. This can be accomplished using light gates and an electronic timer or computer. You will probably have carried out experiments on this, and although the details may vary the basic principles will be the same.

Using a Single Light Gate and Double Card
The double card breaks the light beam twice and the times of these two events are measured by the timer. The first section allows the initial velocity to be calculated and the second section will be used to calculate the final velocity. The time between the initial and final velocities is also recorded automatically.

If a computer is used to automatically calculate the acceleration the length of the card will have to be entered into a software program.

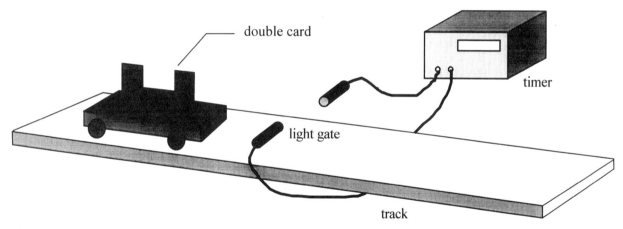

The apparatus shown above can easily be modified so that a single card is used along with two light gates. This again gives an initial and final velocity so allowing acceleration to be calculated.

Graphs of Motion
Information about the motion of an object can be obtained from velocity-time graphs and acceleration-time graphs.

The three simplest velocity-time graphs are shown below along with the equivalent acceleration-time graphs.

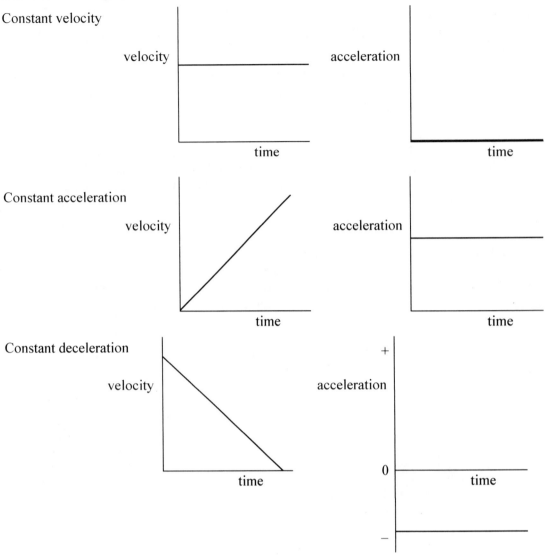

Constant velocity

Constant acceleration

Constant deceleration

Remember that both velocity and acceleration are vector quantities. You will notice that the graph of deceleration is below the x axis i.e. it is **negative**. Since acceleration is a vector quantity the graph must indicate direction as well as magnitude. The acceleration is therefore said to be positive and the deceleration, since it is caused by the force acting in the opposite direction, negative.

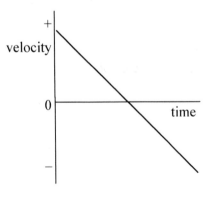

The graphs shown here are for the same motion. On the left is the velocity-time graph and on the right the speed-time graph for the same motion.

No account is taken of the direction of travel of the object in the speed-time graph.

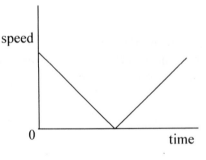

Additional Information from Graphs

The gradient of a velocity-time graph can be used to calculate the value of acceleration.
If the gradient does not change then neither does the acceleration.

The area under a velocity-time graph will give a value for displacement. Remember that the area above the *x* axis will indicate the displacement in one direction and the area below the *x* axis the displacement in the opposite direction.

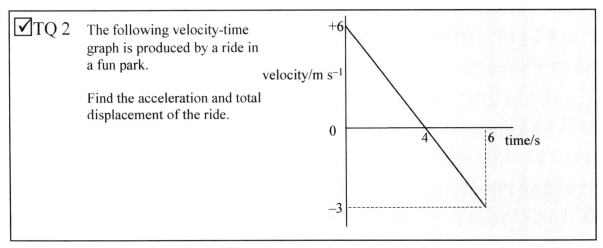

✔TQ 2   The following velocity-time graph is produced by a ride in a fun park.

Find the acceleration and total displacement of the ride.

The Equations of Motion

There are three equations known as the equations of motion which are applied to solve problems in kinematics and these are:

1 —— $v = u + at$

2 —— $s = ut + \frac{1}{2}at^2$

3 —— $v^2 = u^2 + 2as$

where u = initial velocity at start of time interval measured in metres per second (m s^{-1})

v = final velocity after time t measured in metres per second (m s^{-1})

a = acceleration during time t measured in metres per second per second (m s^{-2})

s = displacement during time t measured in metres (m)

t = time over which acceleration occurs measured in seconds (s)

These equations only apply to the motion of an object which is experiencing a constant value of acceleration in a straight line. Velocity, acceleration and displacement are all vectors and so direction must be taken into account by making the values of these terms either positive or negative.

Deriving the Equations of Motion

The three equations of motion can be derived as shown below.

1 —— $v = u + at$

Acceleration is defined as the rate of change of velocity so $a = \dfrac{v - u}{t}$

This can be rearranged to give $v = u + at$

$2 \underline{\hspace{1cm}} s = ut + \tfrac{1}{2}at^2$

Consider the following velocity-time graph of an object accelerating from an initial velocity u to a final velocity v in a time of t seconds.

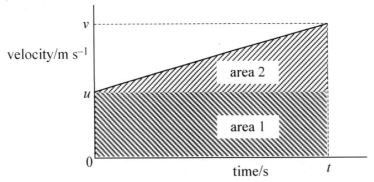

Displacement s is given by the area under the velocity-time graph

$$s = \text{area } 1 + \text{area } 2$$
$$s = ut + \tfrac{1}{2} \times t \times (v - u)$$
$$s = ut + \tfrac{1}{2} \times t \times at \qquad \text{because } v = u + at \text{ gives us } v - u = at$$
$$s = ut + \tfrac{1}{2}at^2$$

$3 \underline{\hspace{1cm}} v^2 = u^2 + 2as$

Equations 1 and 2 can be combined to give an equation which does not include time t.

Square equation 1
$$v^2 = (u + at)^2$$
$$v^2 = u^2 + 2uat + a^2t^2$$
$$v^2 = u^2 + 2a(ut + \tfrac{1}{2}at^2)$$
$$\text{since } s = ut + \tfrac{1}{2}at^2$$
$$v^2 = u^2 + 2as$$

Using the Equations of Motion

The three equations of motion can be applied to any situation where there is uniform acceleration. This may be motion resulting from the effects of gravity or could be from other causes such as a vehicle accelerating along a road.

It is strongly recommended that you use the following method in solving equation of motion problems. Learn the steps involved and apply them to every problem.

- Make a list of the variables u, v, a, s and t.

- If there is motion in two directions decide which will be positive and which negative.

- Write down any quantities given in the question—look especially for values not explicitly given but which you know from the physics of the situation.

- Decide which equation of motion will allow you to find the answer you need—you may have to use two formulae in succession with some problems.

HINT:-   If you are unable to progress in a problem then ask yourself "What else can I calculate?" Usually this will lead you on to finding the answer.

- Set out your calculations neatly.

- Underline your final answer or write it out in a sentence.

Example: A Mini is travelling at 25 m s⁻¹ when it starts to decelerate at 3 m s⁻². What will be the velocity of the Mini after it has covered a distance of 60 m?

Answer: $u = 25$ m s⁻¹
            $v = ?$
            $a = -3$ m s⁻² (note that this value is negative as initial velocity is positive)
            $s = 60$ m
            $t = ?$

$$v^2 = u^2 + 2\,a\,s$$
$$v^2 = 25^2 + 2 \times \text{-}3 \times 60$$
$$v^2 = 625 - 360$$
$$v = \sqrt{265}$$
$$v = 16 \cdot 3 \text{ m s}^{-1}$$

Velocity of Mini after travelling 60 m is 16·3 m s⁻¹ forwards.

☑TQ 3   A rabbit accelerates from rest at a rate of 8 m s⁻². For what length of time had the rabbit been running when it had covered a distance of 20 m?

Using the Equations of Motion with Gravity
Most of the problems you will be required to solve involve motion due to gravity. The types of question fall into **three** main categories and by carefully examining the type of questions you are likely to be asked it is possible to anticipate some of the problems.

The **three** categories of problems are:
- objects dropped or projected vertically upwards;
- objects projected horizontally;
- objects projected at an angle.

Objects Dropped or Projected Vertically Upwards
If an object is either dropped or projected vertically upwards then gravity will provide a force attracting it towards the ground. Since we are dealing with a vector motion then one direction must be made positive and the other negative. The commonest convention is to make any velocity upwards positive and any velocity downwards negative. **Since gravity always acts downwards it is always negative**—no matter in what direction the object is travelling. (You may have been taught that the downwards direction is positive—this is OK, just stick to whichever convention you have been taught.)

Note that the effects of friction are usually ignored and do not enter into any calculations made.

HINTS:
- If an object is dropped its initial velocity will be 0 m s⁻¹.
- If it is thrown up into the air its velocity at its maximum height will be 0 m s⁻¹.
- If an object is thrown into the air and allowed to fall back to the same height its upward motion will exactly mirror its downwards motion.
- The symbol for acceleration due to gravity is g. In examinations g usually has the value of $-9\cdot8$ m s⁻² but **check this at the front of the exam paper to make sure!**

Example: A ball is thrown into the air with a velocity of 6 m s^{-1}. How long will it take to reach its maximum height and what will this height be?

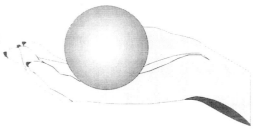

Answer $u = 6$ m s^{-1}
$v = 0$ m s^{-1}
$a = -9 \cdot 8$ m s^{-2}
$s = ?$
$t = ?$

Time to reach maximum height.

$v = u + at$

$0 = 6 + -9 \cdot 8\, t$

$9 \cdot 8\, t = 6$

$t = \dfrac{6}{9 \cdot 8}$

$t = 0 \cdot 61$ s

time taken to reach maximum height is 0·61 s

Maximum height reached.

$v^2 = u^2 + 2\, a\, s$

$0^2 = 6^2 + 2 \times -9 \cdot 8 \times s$

$0 = 36 - 19 \cdot 6\, s$

$19 \cdot 6\, s = 36$

$s = 1 \cdot 8$ m

maximum height reached was 1·8 m

Objects Projected Horizontally

You will recall from Standard Grade Physics that a projectile has a combination of vertical motion and horizontal motion and that the these two motions are independent of one another. In the vertical direction the object undergoes acceleration due to gravity. In the horizontal direction the object travels with a constant velocity. As a result the equations of motion are used only with the vertical component and the equation for constant velocity, $\text{velocity} = \dfrac{\text{distance}}{\text{time}}$ ($v = \dfrac{s}{t}$), is used for the horizontal component.

HINTS:

- The horizontal and vertical motion must be considered independently of one another.

- The initial vertical velocity will be 0 m s^{-1} no matter what the value of horizontal velocity.

- When extracting information from the question lay it out as shown below so that the information relevant to the vertical and horizontal motion is clearly seen.

Vertical	Horizontal
$u_v =$	$v_h =$
$v_v =$	$s_h =$
$a =$	$t =$
$s_v =$	
$t =$	

- The time t is the same for both the horizontal and vertical motion. If you work out this information for one column then put it in the other also.

Example: A ball rolls off the end of a horizontal table with a velocity of 1·5 m s⁻¹. It lands a distance of 0·8 m from the base of the table. Find the height of the table.

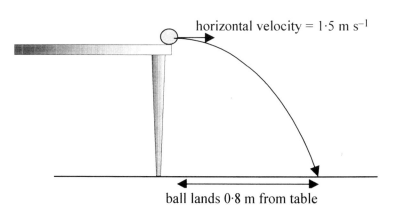

horizontal velocity = 1·5 m s⁻¹

ball lands 0·8 m from table

Answer:

Vertical
$u_v = 0$ m s⁻¹
$v_v = ?$
$a = -9·8$ m s⁻²
$s_v = ?$
$t = ?$

Horizontal
$v_h = 1·5$ m s⁻¹
$s_h = 0·8$ m
$t = ?$

Consider the horizontal motion to find the time of flight.

$$v_h = \frac{s_h}{t}$$

$$1·5 = \frac{0·8}{t}$$

$$t = 0·53 \text{ s}$$

Time of 0·53 s can now be used with vertical component.

$$s_v = u_v t + \tfrac{1}{2} a t^2$$

$$s_v = 0 \times 0·53 + \tfrac{1}{2} \times -9·8 \times 0·53^2$$

$$s_v = -1·4 \text{ m}$$

Displacement is 1·4 m downwards so table is 1·4 m in height.

Objects Projected at an Angle
The last category of projectile question to be considered is one where the projectile is projected with an initial velocity at an angle to the horizontal as in the example shown below.

velocity of 25 m s⁻¹ at angle of 30° above the horizontal

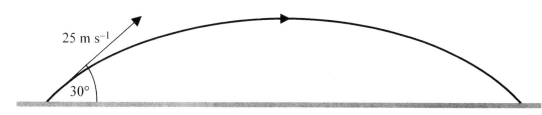

25 m s⁻¹

30°

The velocity of 25 m s⁻¹ is made up of a horizontal and vertical component and it is these components which must be used in any calculations carried out.

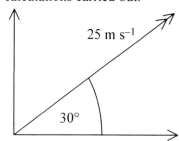

25 m s⁻¹

30°

vertical component, $v_v = v \sin \theta$
$v_v = 25 \sin 30°$
$v_v = 12·5$ m s⁻¹

horizontal component, $v_h = v \cos \theta$
$v_h = 25 \cos 30°$
$v_h = 21·7$ m s⁻¹

The components can be represented in graphical form as shown below.

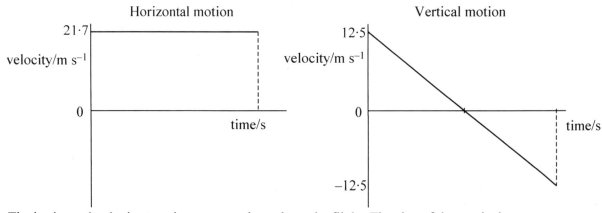

The horizontal velocity remains constant throughout the flight. The size of the vertical component decreases until the projectile is at maximum height, then becomes negative and increases as the projectile falls i.e. vertical velocity constantly decreases.

HINTS:
- The resultant velocity **must** be split into the horizontal and vertical components to be used in calculations.

- The horizontal and vertical motion **must** be considered independently of one another.

- It can be useful to consider the flight of the projectile in two halves—the first half from launch to maximum height and the second half from maximum height to landing.

- The vertical velocity at maximum height is 0 m s^{-1}.

- The two halves of the flight can be thought of as mirror images of each other.

Example: A tennis ball strikes the ground and bounces with a velocity of 8 m s^{-1} at an angle of 60° above the horizontal. Find:
   (i)   the vertical and horizontal component of the ball's velocity;
   (ii)   the time taken for the ball to reach maximum height;
   (iii)   how far from where it bounced the ball landed.

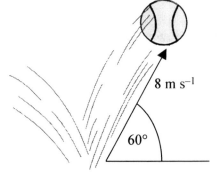

Answer: (i)   vertical component, $u_v = v \sin \theta$ horizontal component, $v_h = v \cos \theta$

$$u_v = 8 \sin 60°$$
$$v_h = 8 \cos 60°$$
$$u_v = 6 \cdot 9 \text{ m s}^{-1}$$
$$v_h = 4 \cdot 0 \text{ m s}^{-1}$$

(ii)   <u>Vertical</u>
$u_v = 6 \cdot 9$ m s^{-1}
$v_v = 0$ m s^{-1}
$a = -9 \cdot 8$ m s^{-2}
$s_v = ?$
$t = ?$

<u>Horizontal</u>
$v_h = 4 \cdot 0$ m s^{-1}
$s_h = ?$
$t = ?$

Use vertical motion to find the time to maximum height.

$$v_v = u_v + at$$
$$0 = 6 \cdot 9 + -9 \cdot 8 \, t$$
$$-6 \cdot 9 = -9 \cdot 8 \, t$$
$$t = \frac{-6 \cdot 9}{-9 \cdot 8}$$
$$t = 0 \cdot 7 \text{ s}$$

Time to maximum height is $0 \cdot 7$ s

(ii) To find the time for the whole flight double the time to maximum height.

$$\text{time of flight} = 2 \times 0\cdot7$$
$$\text{time of flight} = 1\cdot4 \text{ s}$$

Horizontal
$v_h = 4\cdot0 \text{ m s}^{-1}$
$s_h = ?$
$t = 1\cdot4 \text{ s}$

$$v_h = \frac{s_h}{t}$$

$$4\cdot0 = \frac{s_h}{1\cdot4}$$

$$s_h = 5\cdot6 \text{ m}$$

horizontal distance travelled is 5·6 m.

☑TQ 4 A football is kicked with a velocity of 12 m s^{-1} at an angle of 30° above the horizontal.

Find (i) Find the horizontal and vertical components of the ball's motion.

(ii) Find the maximum height reached by the ball.

(iii) What horizontal distance will the ball reach?

Newton's Second Law, Energy and Power

From Standard Grade

This section of the syllabus deals with the forces which cause motion and the properties of a moving system. As with most of the Higher syllabus, a number of important ideas were introduced in Standard Grade.

Newton's First Law—"An object will remain at rest or will continue to move in a straight line at constant speed unless acted on by an unbalanced force."

Newton's Second Law—"The acceleration produced in a body is directly proportional to the unbalanced force applied and inversely proportional to the mass of the body."
This is expressed in the equation $F = m\,a$.

When a force of 1 N is applied to a mass of 1 kg it will produce an acceleration of 1 m s^{-2}. It is the **unbalanced force** which is important. Often a number of forces will act on an object, but it is only if there is an overall unbalanced force that acceleration will be produced. We can write the above equation in the form:

$$F_{un} = m\,a$$

F_{un} = unbalanced force in newtons (N)
m = mass in kilograms (kg)
a = acceleration in metres per second per second (m s^{-2})

Solving $F_{un} = m\,a$ Problems

A careful analysis of any situation presented in a problem is required before attempting to solve it. The steps you should take are as follows:

- Draw a sketch of the situation marking all forces and masses.

- Find the unbalanced force and apply $F_{un} = m\,a$ to the whole system if appropriate.

- Indicate on the diagram the direction of the acceleration of the object selected.

- If only part of the system is to be analysed, sketch it and mark on the mass and forces acting on it.

- Apply $F_{un} = m\,a$ to the selected part of the system where F_{un} is the unbalanced force acting on the object.

Example 1:   On takeoff, the engines of a rocket produce a thrust of 300 kN. Calculate the acceleration of the rocket if it has a mass of 6000 kg. (Take g as 9·8 N kg^{-1})

- Draw a sketch of the situation marking all forces and masses.

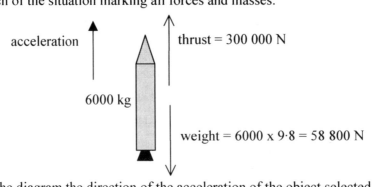

- Indicate on the diagram the direction of the acceleration of the object selected.

- Find the unbalanced force and apply $F_{un} = m\,a$ to the whole system if appropriate.

The unbalanced force is upwards and is equal to thrust minus weight

$$F_{un} = 300\ 000 - 58\ 800$$
$$= 241\ 200 \text{ N}$$

$$F_{un} = m\,a$$
$$241\ 200 = 6000\,a$$
$$a = \frac{241\ 200}{6000}$$
$$a = 40 \cdot 2 \text{ m s}^{-2}$$

The initial acceleration of the rocket is 40·2 m s^{-2} upwards.

Example 2: A train consists of an engine with two carriages. The engine has a mass of 40 000 kg and each carriage has a mass of 5000 kg. The pulling force provided by the engine is 25 000 N and there are frictional forces of 2000 N on **each** carriage and the engine.

(*a*) Calculate the acceleration of the train.

(*b*) On leaving a station the train accelerates at 1·5 m s^{-2}. Find the tension in the coupling between the last carriage and the rest of the train. (Assume there are still 2000 N of frictional forces on the carriage.)

Answer: (*a*)
- Draw a sketch of the situation marking all forces and masses.

- Find the unbalanced force and apply $F_{un} = m\,a$ to the whole system if appropriate;

$$\text{Total mass} = 40\ 000 + 5000 + 5000 = 50\ 000 \text{ kg}$$
$$F_{un} = 25\ 000 - (3 \times 2000) = 19\ 000 \text{ N}$$
$$F_{un} = m\,a$$
$$19\ 000 = 50\ 000\,a$$
$$a = \frac{19\ 000}{50\ 000}$$
$$a = 0 \cdot 38 \text{ m s}^{-2}$$

Answer: (*b*)
- If only part of the system is to be analysed sketch it and mark the mass and forces acting on it.

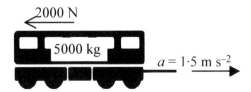

- Apply $F_{un} = m\,a$ to the selected part of the system where F is the unbalanced force acting on the object.

$$F_{un} = m\,a$$
$$F_{un} = 5000 \times 1{\cdot}5$$
$$F_{un} = 7500\text{ N}$$

Tension must produce acceleration and overcome friction.
Tension $= 7500 + 2000$ N
Tension $= 9500$ N

Total tension in coupling is 9500 N.

☑TQ 5　A caravan with a mass of 400 kg is being towed by a car. Calculate the tension in the tow-bar between the car and caravan if the car accelerates at 2 m s⁻². The frictional forces acting on the caravan are 4000 N.

Forces and Vectors

Forces are vector quantities and are treated as described on pages 1 to 4. A situation which frequently occurs in examination questions is where two forces act on an object at an angle. The arrangement in a typical question is shown below.

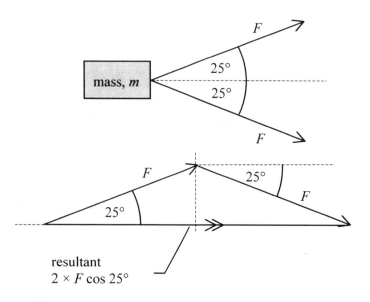

resultant
$2 \times F \cos 25°$

The two forces must be added as vectors to find the resultant force pulling the mass. This is achieved by redrawing the forces as shown in the second diagram.

Two right angled triangles have been produced so the resultant force forwards is the equivalent of $2 \times F \cos 25°$ The direction of the resultant is horizontally forwards.

This 'trick' of creating two right angled triangles **only** works when the forces are of equal size and are at the same angle to the horizontal. In other cases a scale diagram must be drawn to find the resultant.

☑TQ 6　Find the acceleration of the mass shown in the diagram opposite.

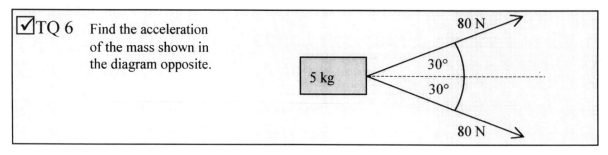

The Special Case of the Lift

A frequent examination problem involves the apparent change in weight of a person standing in a lift. This can be demonstrated by the person standing in a lift and observing their weight on a set of bathroom scales as the lift accelerates or decelerates up and down the lift shaft. It is important to realise that the bathroom scales indicate the force being applied upwards on the person standing on the scales.

In situations where the lift is stationary or where velocity is constant, either up or down, the upwards force registered by the scales is equal to the person's weight. If the lift accelerates however, the scales must read the person's weight plus the unbalanced force required to produce that motion. That unbalanced force may be positive or negative depending on the direction of motion.

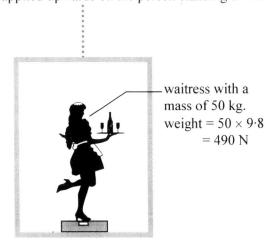

waitress with a mass of 50 kg.
weight = 50×9.8
= 490 N

In each of the cases described below there is an acceleration of 1 m s^{-2} where $F_{un} = m\,a$ so $F_{un} = 50 \times 1 = 50$ N.

Lift accelerates at 1 m s^{-2} travelling upwards:– The scales must balance person's weight and provide the extra unbalanced force to accelerate the person's mass upwards i.e. 490 N + 50 N = 540 N.

Lift decelerates at 1 m s^{-2} travelling upwards:– The scales must balance person's weight but allow an unbalanced force downwards to allow the person to decelerate i.e. 490 N – 50 N = 440 N.

Lift accelerates at 1 m s^{-2} travelling downwards:– The scales must push with a force equal to the person's weight less 50 N so that there will be an unbalanced force downwards of 50 N i.e. 490 N – 50 N = 440 N.

Lift decelerates at 1 m s^{-2} travelling downwards:– The scales must balance person's weight and provide an unbalanced force upwards of 50 N to slow the person down i.e. 490 N + 50 N = 540 N.

Note:
- The weight of the person does not actually change during any journey—only the force which is measured on the scales.

- If the lift cable breaks and the lift falls freely then the scales will read zero. The person in the lift accelerates at 9·8 m s^{-2} downwards and the force required for this is the same as the person's weight. As a result the scales must read zero.

☑TQ 7   A pupil with a mass of 60 kg stands in the school lift on a set of bathroom scales.

(a)   What will the scales read when the lift is stationary?

(b)   The lift accelerates downwards at 2 m s^{-2}. What will the scales now read?

Forces at an Angle
A small truck is pulled by a force, F, at an angle θ.

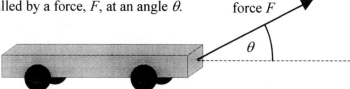

The force can be divided into a horizontal componeı   component.

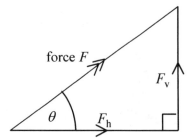

The vertical component of the force F_v can be found by trigonometry so:

vertical component $F_v = F \sin \theta$

The horizontal component of the force F_h is also found by trigonometry so:

horizontal component $F_h = F \cos \theta$

The vector components can be redrawn as shown below.

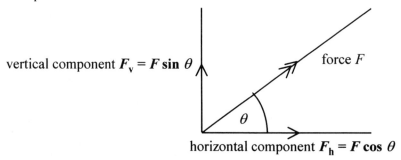

vertical component $\boldsymbol{F_v = F \sin \theta}$ force F

horizontal component $\boldsymbol{F_h = F \cos \theta}$

Forces on a Slope
A force can also be resolved into its components when a mass is resting on a slope. In this case the object's weight is split into components parallel and perpendicular to the slope as shown below.

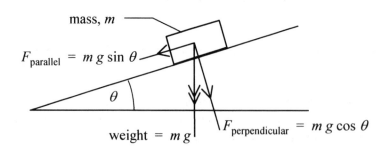

mass, m

$F_{parallel} = m\,g \sin \theta$

weight $= m\,g$

$F_{perpendicular} = m\,g \cos \theta$

The weight of the mass acts vertically downwards. The weight is a vector which can be split into two components.

- $F_{perpendicular}$ acting at right angles to the slope pulls object against slope.

- $F_{parallel}$ acting parallel to the slope, causes acceleration down the slope.

$$F_{perpendicular} = \text{weight of mass} \times \cos\theta \qquad \boldsymbol{F_{perpendicular} = mg \cos\theta}$$

$$F_{parallel} = \text{weight of mass} \times \sin\theta \qquad \boldsymbol{F_{parallel} = mg \sin\theta}$$

If an object is at rest on a slope—or moving down it at a steady speed—then the forces acting on the object must be balanced. Any frictional forces present must be equal and opposite to the component of weight parallel with the slope.

When analysing motion of a mass on a ramp it is only the forces parallel with the ramp which play a part in determining the motion of the mass. The perpendicular component is balanced by the reaction force of the ramp. In the instance shown below the component of weight, $F_{parallel}$, and the frictional force, $F_{friction}$, must be added together as vectors and the resultant force, F_{un}, used in the equation $F_{un} = m\,a$.

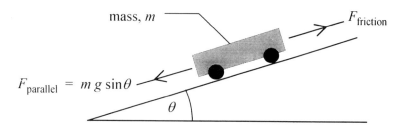

$F_{parallel} = m\,g\,\sin\theta$

☑TQ 8   A trolley with a mass of 2 kg rests on a slope which is raised at an angle of 10° above the horizontal.

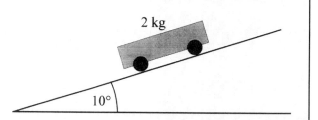

2 kg

10°

(a)   What is the component of the trolley's weight acting parallel with the slope?

(b)   A force of 1·6 N parallel and down the slope is now applied to the trolley. What will be the acceleration of the trolley if the force of friction against the motion of the trolley is 2 N?

Momentum and Impulse

Momentum
In Physics, we define momentum as the product of mass and velocity i.e.

momentum = mass × velocity   where   momentum is measured in kilograms metres per second (kg m s^{-1})

momentum = $m \times v$ m = mass measured in kilograms (kg)

                                          v = velocity measured in metres per second (m s^{-1})

Momentum is a **vector** quantity. We will consider only motion back and forth along a straight line. Vehicles travelling in opposite directions will have positive momentum and negative momentum.

Collisions
If two objects interact by colliding together it is possible to apply the law of conservation of momentum. This states that the **total momentum before a collision will be equal to the total momentum after a collision, providing there are no external forces acting**. This law can also be applied to explosions where an object breaks into two pieces which are ejected in opposite directions, such as a rocket ejecting hot gases during its launch.

Collisions can be categorised as either inelastic or elastic.

Inelastic Collisions
An inelastic collision is defined as one in which total momentum is conserved but the total kinetic energy is not. A good example of an inelastic collision could be where a dart strikes and embeds itself in a dartboard. A collision may still be inelastic even if the objects do not lock together. If a car collides with another car and the two cars separate after the collision the collision will still have been inelastic as **kinetic energy was lost** i.e. converted into heat and sound.

Solving Momentum Problems
A typical inelastic momentum problem is shown below.

Two vehicles rest on a linear air track. Vehicle 1 is projected at 0·5 m s^{-1} towards vehicle 2 which is stationary. Both vehicles have a mass of 0·75 kg. A cork and pin are used to lock the vehicles together after they collide. What will be the velocity of the vehicles after the collision?

vehicle 1   0·5 m s^{-1} vehicle 2   at rest

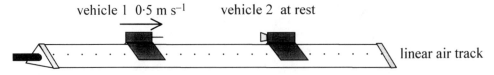

linear air track

Just as in kinematics problems, you should structure your answer carefully to eliminate errors. It is often very useful to sketch the situation marking on all values for mass and velocity.

total momentum before = total momentum after   Write this statement at the start of your answer.

$$(m_1 u_1) + (m_2 u_2) = (m_1 + m_2)v$$

$$(0 \cdot 75 \times 0 \cdot 5) + (0 \cdot 75 \times 0) = (0 \cdot 75 + 0 \cdot 75)v$$

Where vehicles remain locked together after the collision they can be regarded as a single vehicle.

$$0 \cdot 375 + 0 = 1 \cdot 5\, v$$

$$v = \frac{0 \cdot 375}{1 \cdot 5}$$

$$v = 0 \cdot 25 \text{ m s}^{-1}$$

The velocity of the vehicles after the collision is 0·25 m s^{-1} to the right.

In some questions the objects will be travelling in opposite directions. Since velocity is a vector, one of the directions is made positive and one negative. For example, suppose vehicle 2 in the question above was not at rest but travelled from right to left at $1 \cdot 0$ m s^{-1}. What would now be the velocity of the vehicles after they collide and lock together?

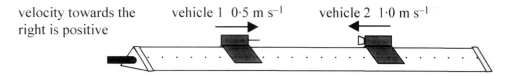

velocity towards the right is positive

vehicle 1 $0 \cdot 5$ m s^{-1}

vehicle 2 $1 \cdot 0$ m s^{-1}

total momentum before = total momentum after

$$(m_1 u_1) + (m_2 u_2) = (m_1 + m_2)v$$
$$(0 \cdot 75 \times 0 \cdot 5) + (0 \cdot 75 \times -1) = (0 \cdot 75 + 0 \cdot 75)v$$
$$0 \cdot 375 + (-0 \cdot 75) = 1 \cdot 5 \text{ v}$$
$$-0 \cdot 375 = 1 \cdot 5 \text{ v}$$
$$v = \frac{-0 \cdot 375}{1 \cdot 5}$$
$$v = -0 \cdot 25 \ m \ s^{-1}$$

The final velocity of the two vehicles is $0 \cdot 25$ m s^{-1} to the left.

☑TQ 9   A trolley with a mass of $1 \cdot 5$ kg travelling at 4 m s^{-1} collides with a second stationary trolley which has a mass of $2 \cdot 0$ kg. After the collision the trolleys remain locked together. Calculate the velocity of the trolleys after the collision.

Elastic collisions
In elastic collisions the two colliding objects do not stick together but remain separate after the collision.

Trolley A with a mass of $0 \cdot 2$ kg travelling at 10 m s^{-1} runs into the back of a second trolley B with a mass of 1 kg travelling in the same direction at 1 m s^{-1}.

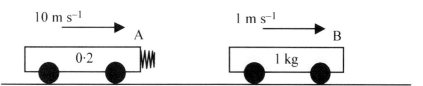

10 m s^{-1} A

1 m s^{-1} B

$0 \cdot 2$ 1 kg

After the collision trolley A rebounds backwards with a velocity of 5 m s^{-1}. Find the velocity and direction of travel of trolley B.

total momentum before = total momentum after

$$(m_A u_A) + (m_B u_B) = (m_A v_A) + (m_B v_B)$$
$$(0 \cdot 2 \times 10) + (1 \times 1) = (0 \cdot 2 \times -5) + (1 v_B)$$
$$2 + 1 = -1 + 1 v_B$$
$$4 = v_B$$
$$v_B = 4 \text{ m s}^{-1}$$

Since vehicle A and B move off separately after the collision their velocities could be different so they are treated as separate vehicles after the collision.

Velocity of trolley B is 4 m s^{-1} to the right.

☑TQ 10   A child throws a ball at a coconut in a fun-fair stall. The ball has a mass of $0 \cdot 1$ kg and is travelling at 5 m s^{-1} when it hits the coconut. If the ball now falls vertically to the floor what will be the velocity of the coconut if it has a mass of $0 \cdot 4$ kg?

Proof of elasticity

In an elastic collision both momentum and kinetic energy are conserved i.e. not only will the total momentum before and after the collision be the same but the total kinetic energy before and after the collision will be the same. This can be demonstrated for the example above by calculating the total kinetic energy before and after the collision.

$$
\begin{aligned}
\text{Total } E_K \text{ before collision} &= (\tfrac{1}{2}m_A\, u_A{}^2) + (\tfrac{1}{2}m_B\, u_B{}^2) \\
&= (\tfrac{1}{2} \times 0\cdot2 \times 10^2) + (\tfrac{1}{2} \times 1 \times 1^2) \\
&= 10 + 0\cdot5 \\
&= 10\cdot5 \text{ J}
\end{aligned}
$$

$$
\begin{aligned}
\text{Total } E_K \text{ after collision} &= (\tfrac{1}{2}m_A\, v_A{}^2) + (\tfrac{1}{2}m_B\, v_B{}^2) \\
&= (\tfrac{1}{2} \times 0\cdot2 \times 5^2) + (\tfrac{1}{2} \times 1 \times 4^2) \\
&= 2\cdot5 + 8 \\
&= 10\cdot5 \text{ J}
\end{aligned}
$$

The total kinetic energy before and after the collision can be seen to be the same so the collision is elastic—sometimes described as **perfectly elastic**.

Explosions

An explosion is a situation where an object 'explodes' into two parts which then travel in opposite directions. Before the event the total momentum is zero since the velocity of the object will be zero. After the 'explosion' the parts move in opposite directions so v_1 and v_2 will have opposite signs i.e. one will be negative and the other positive. The momentum of each part will be the same size but opposite in sign so that when added together they give zero and thus momentum is conserved.

The following example shows a situation where the principle of conservation of momentum can be applied to an explosion.

A rocket has a mass of 400 kg and is loaded with 260 kg of fuel. It ejects hot exhaust gases from its engine at 500 m s^{-1}. Calculate the velocity of the rocket once all the fuel has been used up.

total momentum before = total momentum after

$$
\left(m_R u_R\right) + \left(m_F u_F\right) = \left(m_R v_R\right) + \left(m_F v_F\right)
$$

$$
\left(400 \times 0\right) + \left(260 \times 0\right) = \left(400 \times v_R\right) + \left(260 \times -500\right)
$$

$$
0 = 400\, v_R + \; -130\ 000
$$

$$
130\ 000 = 400\, v_R
$$

$$
v_R = \frac{130\ 000}{400}
$$

$$
v_R = 325 \text{ m s}^{-1}
$$

Rocket has a velocity of 325 m s^{-1}.

☑ TQ 11   A disabled boy and his wheelchair have a total mass of 60 kg. From a position sitting in his wheelchair he throws a ball with a mass of 1·5 kg forwards at 8 m s^{-1}. What will be the backwards velocity of the boy and his wheelchair?

Impulse

If a force is applied to a mass for a certain length of time it will cause the mass to accelerate and its velocity will change. The change in velocity means that there will be a change in the momentum of the object which can be calculated as follows:

$$\text{Force} \times \text{time} = \text{change in momentum}$$
$$F\,t = \Delta(m\,v)$$

F = average force in newtons (N)
t = time in seconds (s)
m = mass in kilograms (kg)
v = velocity in metres per second (m s^{-1})

The product of average force and time is called impulse and so,

$$\text{Impulse} = F\,t$$
or
$$\text{Impulse} = \Delta(m\,v)$$

Impulse can be measured in newton seconds (N s)

or

kilograms metres per second (kg m s^{-1})

☑TQ 12 A hockey stick applies an average force of 30 N to a ball with a mass of 0·4 kg. If the ball and stick are in contact for 0·3 s what will be the velocity of the ball?

Many questions in exams relate to the part played by impulse in reducing injuries in road accidents. If a person is brought to rest from a certain velocity there will be a certain change in momentum. The change in momentum will equal the product of F and t. If the time over which the force acts is made as long as possible the force will decrease for the same change in momentum. This is why many safety features such as motorcycle helmets, parts of cars etc. are made so that they crumple in the event of an accident and extend the time of contact and so reduce the average force.

However, a golfer who follows through his or her swing maintains contact with the ball to extend the time of contact with the ball. In this case the force is constant but by increasing the time of contact a greater change in momentum is produced and so the ball travels at a greater velocity.

Force-time graphs

The area under a force-time graph will be equivalent to the impulse or the object's change in momentum. Real life graphs tend to show an increase in force followed by a decline. The two graphs below illustrate how the same impulse or change in momentum can be achieved with either a large or a small force (the area under each graph is identical).

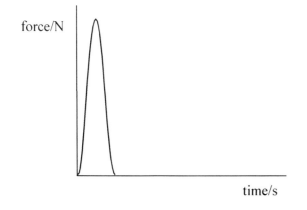

This graph indicates a large force applied over a short period of time.

force/N

This graph indicates a small force applied over a longer period of time.

The impulse is the same in both graphs.

time/s

✓TQ 13 The following force-time graph was obtained when a snooker ball is struck by a cue. The ball has a mass of 0·1 kg.

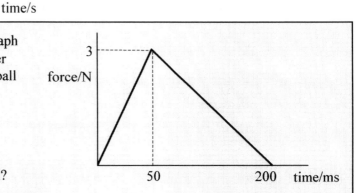

(i)   Calculate the impulse applied to the ball.

(ii) What is the change in momentum of the ball?

(iii) Calculate the velocity of the ball after it is struck.

Here are a few other hints worth remembering.

HINTS:

- If a catapult or spring is used to give a body impulse then the maximum force used to keep it stretched or compressed is **twice the average force** (since the force starts at zero). It is the average force that is used in impulse calculations.

- Some problems involve the conversion of energy e.g. potential energy into kinetic energy, work into kinetic energy etc.

- Remember your formulae from Standard Grade:

  Work, $W = F \times s$,   Power, $P = \dfrac{E}{t}$,   Potential energy, $E_P = m\,g\,h$,

  Kinetic energy, $E_K = \frac{1}{2}m\,v^2$. All these types of energy can be converted from one to another.

Density and Pressure

Density
The density of a substance is its **mass per unit volume**. This is represented by the equation

$$\text{density} = \frac{\text{mass}}{\text{volume}} \qquad \rho = \frac{m}{V}$$

ρ = density in kilograms per cubic metre (kg m^{-3})
m = mass in kilograms (kg)
V = volume in cubic metres (m^3)

The symbol for density is the Greek letter ρ (rho).

✓ TQ 14 A block of perspex has a density of 1190 kg m^{-3}. Calculate the mass of the block if it has a volume of 0·02 m^3.

Measuring the Density of a Gas
There are a variety of methods that can be used to measure the density of a gas. All involve using a balance to find the mass of the gas and a container to hold the gas. Two common methods are described on the next page.

Method 1.
A flask of air is placed on the balance and its mass found. A vacuum pump is then used to evacuate air out of the flask and its mass is measured again. The change in mass is equal to the mass of air removed.

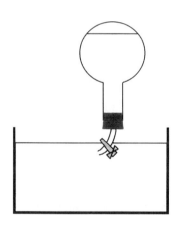

The tube connected to the flask is then opened under water so that water is sucked in to replace the lost air. The volume of this water is equal to the volume of air removed and can be found using a measuring cylinder. Density can now be calculated using the experimental values for mass and volume.

Method 2.
This method is similar to the first. After finding the mass of the flask full of air **additional** air is pumped into the flask. The new mass of the flask is found and the additional mass is equivalent to the mass of the extra air.

By placing the exit tube from the flask under a measuring cylinder full of water the excess air can be released and the volume of the additional air can be measured. The density of air can now be calculated as before.

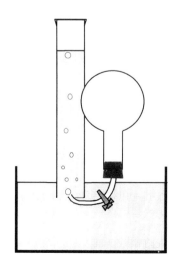

Relative Densities of Solids Liquids and Gases

The density of solids and liquids is much greater than the density of gases. The table below shows some common values to indicate this.

Substance	Density (kg m⁻³)
Iron (solid)	7870
Aluminium (solid)	2700
Water (liquid)	1000
Oxygen (gas)	1·43

The densities of solids and liquids are in thousands of kg m⁻³ whereas the density of gases are much nearer 1 kg m⁻³, approximately 1000 times less. This is because the particles in a gas are spaced much further apart than in a solid or liquid.

The molecules in a solid and liquid are packed closely together. By comparison, the molecules of a gas are approximately ten times further apart.

liquid and solid

gas

Molecules in a gas are **ten** times further apart than molecules in a solid or liquid.

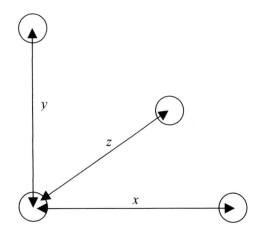

Molecules of a gas are ten times further apart in all directions i.e. in direction x, y and z. This means that the volume of a gas is $10 \times 10 \times 10$ times greater than the volume of the same substance in a solid or liquid form.

For example, a 1 cm³ of carbon dioxide (dry ice) would become almost 1000 cm³ if it were to be heated and change into a gas

Pressure, Force and Area

We frequently talk about the pressure of a car or bicycle tyre. This is caused by the gas molecules in the tyre pushing with a certain force on a certain area of the tyre wall. Pressure may also be produced by the downwards force of an object due to its weight.

Pressure can be defined as the **force per unit area**.

$$\text{pressure} = \frac{\text{force}}{\text{area}}$$

$$p = \frac{F}{A}$$

p = pressure in pascals (Pa) or newtons per square metre (N m^{-2})
F = force in newtons (N)
A = area in square metres (m^2)

A word of warning! If you are given the area in cm^2 or mm^2 remember there are **10 000 cm^2 or 1 000 000 mm^2 in every m^2**.

☑TQ 15 Calculate the force used to press on a rubber stamp if it has an area of 1.5×10^{-3} m^2 and the pressure under the stamp is 10 000 Pa.

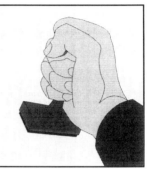

Pressure in a Liquid

If you have ever dived underwater you will appreciate that the deeper you go the greater the pressure—at greater depths the pressure of water on your ear drum can produce discomfort and even pain. Pressure in liquids is dependent upon two factors. These are the **depth** under the liquid and the **density** of liquid involved. The graphs below illustrate this:

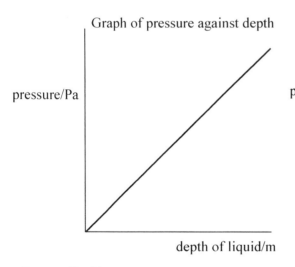

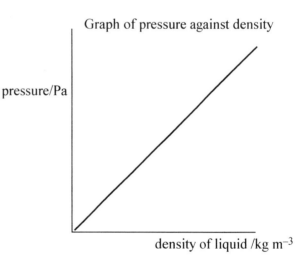

For any liquid

pressure is directly proportional to depth ($p \propto h$)

and   pressure is directly proportional to density ($p \propto \rho$)

The pressure at a certain depth of a liquid with a density ρ can be calculated using the formula:

$$\text{pressure} = \text{density} \times g \times \text{depth}$$

$$p = \rho g h$$

p = pressure in pascals (Pa) or newtons per square metre (N m^{-2})
ρ = density in kilograms per cubic metre (kg m^{-3})
h = depth in metres (m)

✓TQ 16 Atmospheric pressure at the surface of a swimming pool is 1×10^5 Pa. What will be the total pressure at the foot of a swimming pool 5 m deep?
(take g as 10 N kg^{-1})

Buoyancy and Flotation

When an object is placed in a liquid it will experience a force called the buoyancy force or upthrust. All objects experience this whether they float or sink and it is produced by the pressure exerted on the object by the surrounding water.

The dolphin shown in the diagram below experiences a force caused by the water pressure on its upper and lower surface and also on its sides. Remember that the water pressure is greater at greater depths so the pressure on its lower surface is more than on its upper surface. The water pressure on its sides will cancel out.

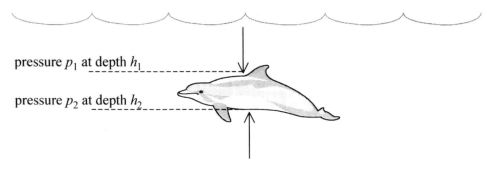

pressure p_1 at depth h_1

pressure p_2 at depth h_2

The pressure on the lower surface of the dolphin is greater than on the upper surface of the dolphin since it is at a greater depth—p_2 is greater than p_1. As a result there is a greater force on the lower surface of the dolphin than on the upper surface This causes a net upward force called the upthrust or buoyancy force.

The buoyancy force will always act upwards. The dolphin will also have weight, acting vertically downwards. It is the relative size of these forces which determines if the dolphin sinks or floats.

If the buoyancy force is greater than the dolphin's weight, it will accelerate upwards.

If the buoyancy force is less than the dolphin's weight, it will accelerate downwards.

If the buoyancy force and the dolphin's weight are the same, there will be no vertical force on the dolphin and it will remain stationary or move at a constant vertical speed.

Note that the rules for buoyancy apply to any **liquid or gas**.

✓TQ 17 A balloon filled with helium has a total mass of 0·015 kg.

(a) Find the unbalanced upward force on the balloon if it has a buoyancy force of 0·177 N.

(b) What will be the acceleration of the balloon?

The Gas Laws

Looking at Pressure of a Gas

The pressure a gas exerts on the walls of the container in which it is enclosed is caused by tiny, invisible gas particles colliding with the walls of the container. There are a great many of these collisions and each one creates a small outward force on the container walls.

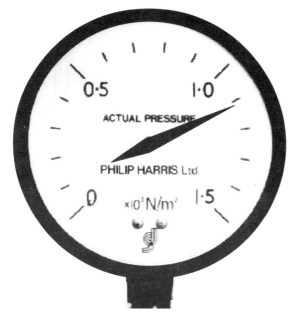

Pressure of a gas can be measured using a device known as a **Bourdon pressure gauge**.

The Bourdon gauge shown opposite has a curved copper tube within it which uncurls as the pressure increases and moves the pointer round.

Normal atmospheric pressure at sea level is 1×10^5 Pa.

Pressure and Volume of a Gas

An experiment can be carried out to investigate the relationship between the pressure and volume of a gas using the apparatus shown below. In this experiment the temperature and the mass of the gas are kept constant.

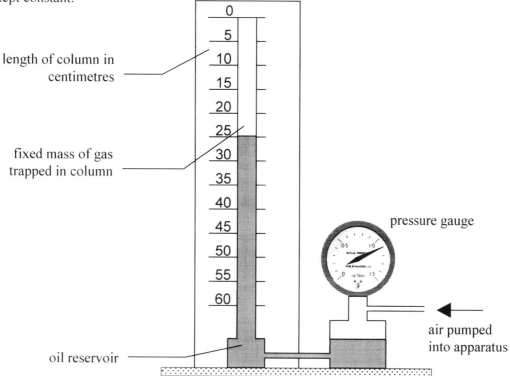

The mass of gas being investigated is trapped in a glass tube by some oil. When air is pumped into the apparatus above the oil reservoir there is an increase in pressure on the oil. This pressure is transferred to the trapped gas and its subsequent volume measured. The temperature of the gas is kept constant by allowing the gas to cool between each change in pressure.

The pressure of the gas is read from the Bourdon gauge and the volume of the gas is measured from a scale marked beside the glass tube. Since the tube has a constant diameter its length will be proportional to its volume.

The results obtained from the experiment allow a graph of pressure against volume to be plotted.

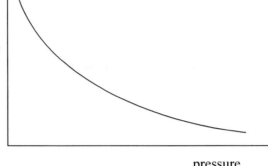

This graph shows **only** that as pressure increases the volume decreases.

If a graph of $\dfrac{1}{\text{volume}}$ against pressure is plotted a straight line through the origin is obtained.

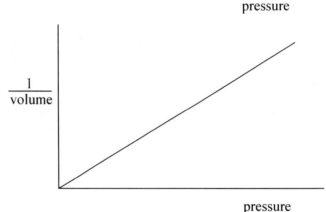

This graph **must** be plotted in order to show the relationship between pressure and volume clearly.

The results of the experiment above show that pressure is indirectly proportional to the volume of gas for a fixed mass of gas at constant temperature.

$$p \propto \frac{1}{V}$$

The relationship between pressure and volume can also be proven mathematically. If two quantities are inversely proportional their product will equal a constant. Hence

$$p \times V = \text{constant}$$

In an examination situation, showing that the product of two values equals a constant is the quickest and simplest way of showing an inverse relationship between the two values. Multiplying all the pairs of values of pressure and volume to give the same number shows that;

$$\text{pressure} \times \text{volume} = \text{constant.}$$

If a gas has initial conditions p_1 and V_1 and the pressure and volume are altered to p_2 and V_2 these are related in the equation

$$p_1 V_1 = p_2 V_2$$

Then above equation is often referred to as Boyle's Law (the Pressure-Volume Law).

NOTE: the units for pressure and volume do not have to be converted into any standard unit—as long as the units are the same on both sides of the equation.

☑TQ 18   A weather balloon has a volume of 2·5 m³ when inflated at sea level where atmospheric pressure is 100 kPa. What will be the volume of the balloon when it has risen to a height where atmospheric pressure is only 40 kPa?

Pressure, Volume and the Kinetic Model

When a gas particle collides with a surface it produces a tiny push or force. Since a gas is made up of countless numbers of these tiny gas particles there will be a huge number of tiny pushes. These combine together to produce gas pressure. If gas is trapped in a container there will be a pressure produced on the walls of the container due to the collisions between the gas particles and the container's walls.

If the volume of the container is reduced, the distance between the container's walls will be reduced. As a result the gas particles do not have to travel as far between collisions with the walls so more collisions will occur in any given period of time and increase the overall force exerted on the walls. This causes an increase in the pressure of the gas.

large volume—few collisions with container walls

small volume—many collisions with container walls

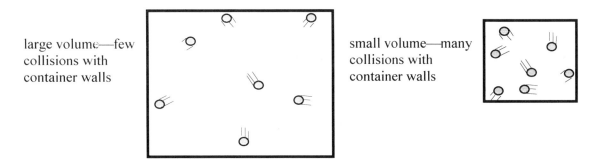

Pressure and Temperature of a Gas

A second experiment can be carried out to investigate the relationship between the pressure and temperature of a gas using the apparatus shown below. In this experiment the volume and the mass of the gas are kept constant.

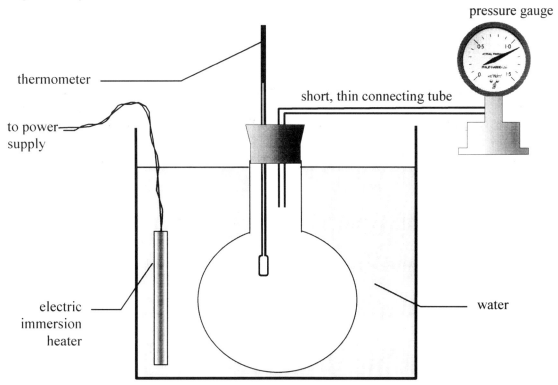

pressure gauge

thermometer

short, thin connecting tube

to power supply

electric immersion heater

water

The flask of gas is submerged in a water bath and the temperature of this is slowly increased using an immersion heater. This in turn raises the temperature of the gas within the flask. The pressure of the gas is measured using a Bourdon pressure gauge and the temperature of the gas is measured using a thermometer placed in the flask.

The results obtained from the experiment allow a graph of pressure against temperature in °C to be plotted.

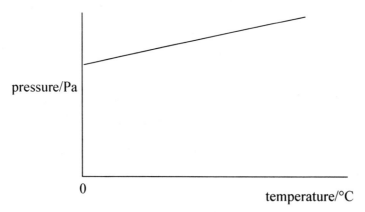

The graph produced as a result shows that the pressure increases with temperature but since it is not a straight line through the origin we cannot say pressure is directly proportional to temperature in °C.

In order to find the relationship between pressure and temperature the pressure/temperature graph must be extended backwards to the point where pressure is zero.

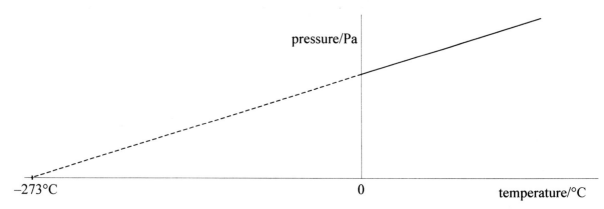

The temperature at which the pressure becomes zero is –273°C. This is known as **absolute zero** and is the starting point or origin for a new temperature scale called the **kelvin** scale. (Absolute zero is the temperature at which the gas particles will cease to move and so exert no pressure.)

Plotting a graph of pressure against temperature in kelvin will produce a straight line through the origin.

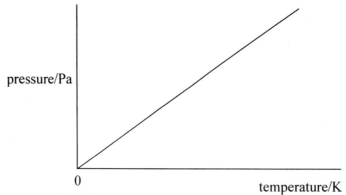

The results of the experiment above show that pressure is directly proportional to the temperature in kelvin for a fixed mass of gas with constant volume:

$$p \propto T \text{ in kelvin}$$

The relationship between pressure and temperature can also be proven mathematically. If two quantities are proportional then dividing one by the other will give a constant. Hence:

$$\frac{p}{T\,(K)} = \text{constant}$$

(In an examination situation, showing that the quotient of two values equals a constant for every set of values is the quickest and simplest way of showing a directly proportional relationship i.e. dividing all the pairs of values of pressure and temperature in kelvin to give the same number.)

If a gas has initial conditions p_1 and T_1 and the pressure and temperature are altered to p_2 and T_2 these are related in the equation

$$\frac{p_1}{T_1} = \frac{p_2}{T_2} \quad \text{providing } T \text{ is in kelvin}$$

The Kelvin and Celsius Scales

The kelvin and celsius temperature scale share the same size of unit, that is 1°C is the same size as 1 K. (Note the lack of the degree (°) symbol before K.) The temperature scales simply have a different starting point.

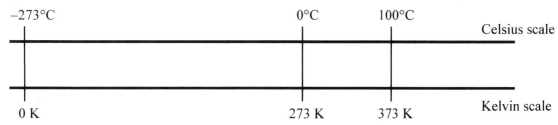

To convert from the **celsius scale to the kelvin scale add 273** e.g. –20°C = 253 K.

To convert from the **kelvin scale to the celsius scale subtract 273** e.g. 323 K = 50°C.

When tackling gas law problems involving temperature the temperature must be converted into kelvin. The final answer may be left in kelvin—there is no need to change back to degrees celsius.

Pressure, Temperature and the Kinetic Model

As the gas heats up the gas particles gain kinetic energy and so move faster. This causes the particles to collide with the container walls more often and with greater force which thus causes an increase in the pressure of the gas.

low temperature—gas particles move slowly and produce few collisions with container walls

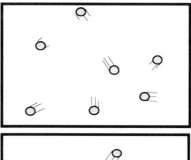

high temperature—gas particles move quickly and produce many collisions with container walls, each collision producing more force on the wall.

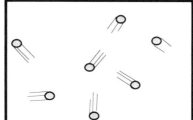

TQ 19 A canister of gas in the cargo hold of an aeroplane is at a temperature of 27°C and contains gas at a pressure of 6×10^5 Pa. What will be the pressure within the container when the temperature of the gas falls to –53°C as the plane flies at high altitude?

Volume and Temperature of a Gas

A third experiment can be carried out to investigate the relationship between the volume and temperature of a gas using the apparatus shown below. In this experiment the pressure and the mass of the gas are kept constant.

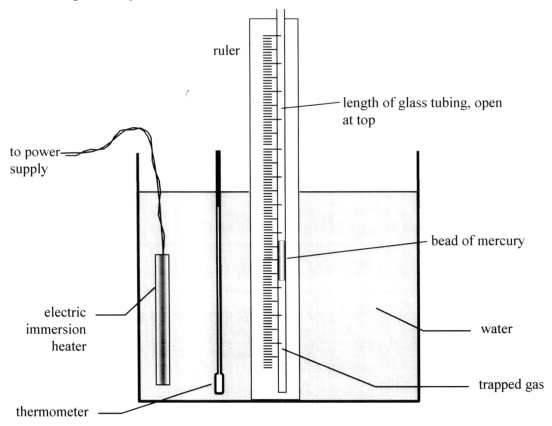

A mass of gas is trapped in a glass tube by a bead of mercury which is free to move up and down the tube. This is placed against a ruler. As the water is heated the trapped gas expands and pushes the mercury up the tube. The length of this trapped gas is taken as a measure of its volume (since the length of the gas is proportional to volume in a tube with a uniform cross section). The pressure of the gas is constant during this experiment.

The results obtained from the experiment allow a graph of volume against temperature in °C to be plotted.

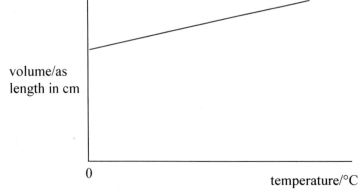

The graph produced as a result shows that the volume increases with temperature but since it is not a straight line through the origin we cannot say volume is directly proportional to temperature in °C. In order to find the relationship between volume and temperature the volume/temperature graph must be extended backwards to the point where volume is zero.

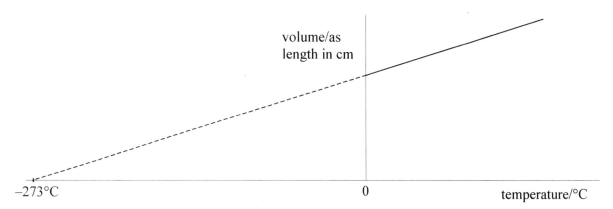

The temperature at which the volume becomes zero is –273°C or absolute zero. This graph is like the one obtained for pressure and temperature in the previous experiment. Plotting a graph of volume against temperature in kelvin will produce a straight line through the origin.

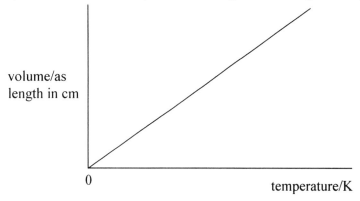

The results of the experiment show that volume is directly proportional to the temperature in kelvin for a fixed mass of gas at constant pressure:

$$V \propto T \text{ in kelvin}$$

The relationship between volume and temperature can also be proven mathematically by dividing the volume by the temperature to give a constant:

$$\frac{V}{T\,(K)} = \text{constant}$$

If a gas has initial conditions V_1 and T_1 and the pressure and temperature are altered to V_2 and T_2 these are related in the equation

$$\frac{V_1}{T_1} = \frac{V_2}{T_2} \text{ providing } T \text{ is in kelvin}$$

Volume, Temperature and the Kinetic Model
As the gas heats up the gas particles gain kinetic energy and so move faster. This causes the particles to collide with the container walls more often and with greater force which thus causes an increase in the pressure of the gas. As a result, the walls of the container are pushed outwards so increasing the volume.

low temperature—gas particles move slowly and produce few collisions with container walls

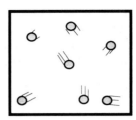

high temperature—gas particles move quickly and produce many collisions with container walls, each collision producing more force on the wall. This causes the walls to be pushed outwards so increasing the volume of the container

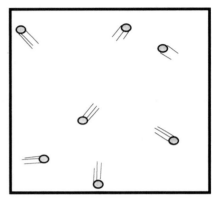

The General Gas Equation
As a result of the three experiments on gases there are now three relationships known.

$$p \times V = \text{constant} \qquad \frac{p}{T\,(\text{K})} = \text{constant} \qquad \frac{V}{T\,(\text{K})} = \text{constant}$$

These three relationships can be combined into a single equation known as the general gas equation.

$$\frac{p_1 V_1}{T_1} = \frac{p_2 V_2}{T_2}$$

Remember, when using this equation always **convert the temperature into Kelvin** before carrying out any calculations.

☑TQ 20   A weather balloon is released at ground level where the temperature is 27°C and the pressure is 1×10^5 Pa. The balloon has a volume of 4 m³. What will be the volume of the balloon when it rises to a height where the pressure is 0.6×10^5 Pa and the temperature is –23°C?

UNIT 2 Electricity and Electronics

Electric Fields and Resistors in Circuits

Electric Fields
There are two types of electric charge, positive and negative. Like charges (positive and positive or negative and negative) repel one another. Unlike charges (positive and negative) attract one another. Around any charged object there is an electric field or area in which an electric charge will experience a force.

Electric fields are invisible but can be made visible using simple techniques. One of these is to place electrodes at high voltage in a dish of oil and sprinkle on semolina powder or grass seeds. These line up along the electric field lines so making them visible.

The diagrams below show the shape of some electric fields. The arrows on the diagrams indicate the direction in which a **positive** charge would move i.e. from positive to negative. The spacing of the field lines indicates the strength of the field—where the lines are closer together the field is stronger.

radial field around a positive charge   uniform field between two parallel plates

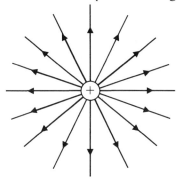 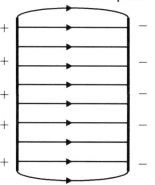

NOTE:
- Although the diagrams above are in two dimensions the field lines are three dimensional and spread in all directions.

- The field lines do not cross.

- In the case of the parallel plates the electric force exerted on a small charge is the same at all points between the plates except at the edge of the plates as the field is not uniform there.

Effect of Placing a Charge in an Electric Field
If an unbalanced force is applied to an object it will cause it to accelerate. This is what can happen to a charge, such as an electron, placed in an electric field. As a result of placing a charge in an electric field it will gain energy. A useful analogy can be made with the effect of moving a mass in a gravitational field.

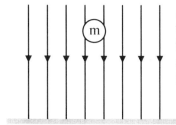 A mass, m, accelerates towards the earth due to the gravitational field and in so doing gains kinetic energy.

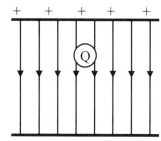 A positive charge, Q, accelerates from the positive to the negative plate due to the electric field and in so doing gains kinetic energy.

The energy that a charge gains when placed in an electric field can be calculated using the formula:

work done on charge $=$ charge $\times$ potential difference through which charge moves

$$W = QV$$

W = energy in joules (J)
Q = charge in coulombs (C)
V = potential difference in volts (V)

The formula $W = QV$ allows us to define the volt. If one joule of work is done in moving one coulomb of charge between two points in an electric field the potential difference (p.d.) between the two points is one volt. Thus 1 volt is equivalent to 1 joule per coulomb.

$$\mathbf{1\,V = 1\,J\,C^{-1}}$$

If a charge is placed in an electric field the energy it gains can be in the form of kinetic energy. This is what happens in an oscilloscope or television tube where electrons are accelerated towards the screen by an electric field. Many questions at Higher are based on this conversion of energy and it is worth remembering that the **work done on a charge is equal to its gain in kinetic energy**.

$$W = QV = \tfrac{1}{2}mv^2$$

If an exam question involves an electron or proton its mass and charge must be known. (This information is not normally given in the question but will be found at the front of the exam paper in the data section.)

☑TQ 21 An electron is accelerated in an oscilloscope by a 4 kV potential. What speed will the electron reach?
(charge on an electron is $-1\cdot60 \times 10^{-19}$ C, mass of electron $= 9\cdot11 \times 10^{-31}$ kg.)

Remember that the maximum speed that can be reached is the speed of light i.e. 3×10^8 m s^{-1}. If you ever get an answer greater than this then check for an error in your calculation!

It is worth recalling here the formula learned in Standard Grade involving charge:

charge $=$ current $\times$ time $\qquad Q = It.$

This formula may have to be used in questions involving charge along with $W = QV$.

Electromotive Force
The electromotive force is the electrical potential energy given to each coulomb of charge which passes through a source. An example of a source could be a 1½ V cell. Each coulomb of charge passing through the cell will gain 1½ joules of energy.

$$\text{i.e. e.m.f.} = \frac{\text{energy}}{\text{charge}} \quad \text{or} \quad V = \frac{W}{Q} \quad \text{as before.}$$

The source could just as easily be a magnet moving in a coil of wire (a generator). As electrons move through a source of e.m.f. they gain energy. In a circuit containing a cell the electrons gain energy as a result of the conversion of chemical energy into electrical energy.

E.m.f. and Circuits

From Ohm's Law ($V = IR$) you will be aware that a component in a circuit which has resistance and has a current flowing through it will have a potential difference across it. When we measure the potential difference (p.d.) across a component in a circuit we are measuring the potential difference between one side of the component and the other.

This potential difference is a measure of the energy lost by the electrons as they flow through the component. Note that energy itself is not lost—it is transformed into another type e.g. in a light bulb it will be converted into heat and light.

Understanding Series and Parallel Circuits

Look at the two circuits below, each containing a 9 V cell, a resistor and a bulb. The first is a series circuit and the second a parallel circuit. You will recall from Standard Grade that potential difference is shared between components in a series circuit but is the same across all components in a parallel circuit.

Series Circuit

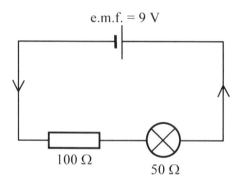

e.m.f. = 9 V

100 Ω   50 Ω

The e.m.f. of the cell is 9 V. This means that every coulomb of charge flowing through the cell will gain 9 J of energy.

As the current flows around the circuit it must lose energy and this will be lost in proportion to the resistance of the component it flows through. Each coulomb of charge will lose 6 J C⁻¹ (6 V) flowing through the resistor and 3 J C⁻¹ (3 V) flowing through the light bulb.

Thus the total energy given up by each coulomb of charge is 9 J, the amount of energy gained by the coulomb of charge from the cell.

Parallel Circuit

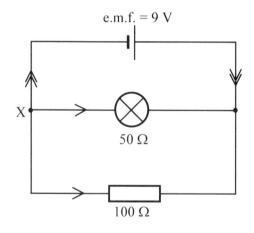

e.m.f. = 9 V

X

50 Ω

100 Ω

This circuit contains a 9 V cell so every coulomb of charge flowing through the cell will gain 9 J of energy.

The charge flows around the circuit but splits at point X with some charge flowing through the bulb and some through the resistor. Any electron will flow through only one component before returning to the cell so the energy which each coulomb of charge is able to give up is 9 J. The electrons therefore give up all their energy at once producing a potential difference across it of 9 V.

Internal Resistance

When electrons travel through a cell they meet a certain amount of resistance. A cell can thus be thought of as a source of e.m.f. in series with an internal resistance r.

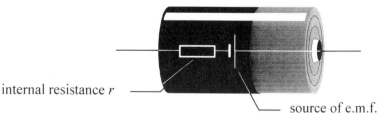

internal resistance r

source of e.m.f.

As a result there will be a potential difference across the internal resistance of the cell called **'lost volts'**—so called because the 'lost volts' are not available or lost to the user of the cell. The potential difference which is available to the cell user across the cell terminals is called the **terminal potential difference (t.p.d.)**. The sum of the 'lost volts' and terminal potential difference will be equal to the total e.m.f. available from the cell.

Summary of definitions:

- e.m.f. = total potential difference available from the cell;
- t.p.d. = potential difference available from terminals of cell;
- 'lost volts' = potential difference across internal resistance of cell.

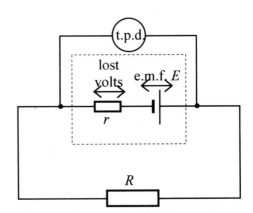

NOTE: There will only be a lost voltage when current is flowing in a circuit. If there is no current flowing through a cell then there will be no 'lost volts' so the potential difference measured across the cell terminals will actually be the e.m.f. One way of measuring the e.m.f. of a cell is to place a high resistance voltmeter across the terminals of the cell and measure the potential difference.

Internal resistance formulae

Look at the diagram below of a cell which has an e.m.f. E, an internal resistance r and an external resistance R. A current I flows around the circuit.

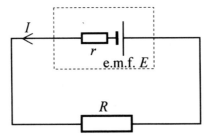

$$e.m.f. = \text{'lost volts'} + t.p.d.$$

since $V = IR$ then $\qquad E = Ir + IR \qquad$ or $\qquad E = I(R + r)$

Your understanding of internal resistance can be helped by trying the two problems below.

Problem 1.

In the circuit shown opposite find:
- (a) The current flowing in the circuit.
- (b) The potential difference across the 2 Ω resistor.
- (c) The potential difference across the 10 Ω resistor.

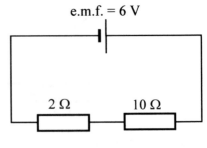

Problem 2.

In the circuit shown opposite find:
- (a) The current flowing in the circuit.
- (b) The 'lost volts'.
- (c) The t.p.d..

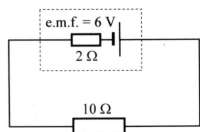

Calculate the answers yourself then turn to the page to see the worked solutions.

Problem 1.

(a) $V = IR$ total resistance $= 12\ \Omega$
    $6 = I \times 12$
    $I = 0{\cdot}5$ A.

(b) $V = IR$
    $V = 0{\cdot}5 \times 2$
    $V = 1$ V

(c) $V = IR$
    $V = 0{\cdot}5 \times 10$
    $V = 5$ V

Problem 2.

(a) E.m.f. $= I(R + r)$
    $6 = I(10 + 2)$
    $I = \dfrac{6}{12}$
    $I = 0{\cdot}5$ A

(b) 'lost volts' $= Ir$
    'lost volts' $= 0{\cdot}5 \times 2$
    'lost volts' $= 1$ V

(c) t.p.d. $= IR$
    t.p.d. $= 0{\cdot}5 \times 10$
    t.p.d. $= 5$ V

If you are observant you should realise that both circuits are really the same i.e. a series circuit containing two resistors. In the second circuit the only difference is that one of the resistors is 'inside' the cell and called an internal resistance. The way the circuits behave and the way they can be treated for solving problems are the same.

☑TQ 22   An 11 Ω resistor is connected in series with a cell of
e.m.f. 3 V and with an internal resistance of 1 Ω.

(a) What will be the reading on the voltmeter
with the switch, S, open?

(b) Find the current flowing through the ammeter
when the switch is closed.

(c) What will be the potential difference across the
terminals of the cell when switch S is closed?

(d) What is the value of the lost volts in the circuit?

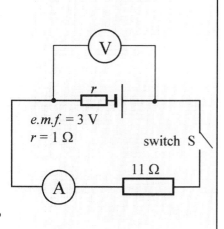

Measuring the E.m.f. of a Cell

The e.m.f. of a cell can most easily be measured by placing a voltmeter across the cell when there is no current flowing. It can also be found by using the circuit shown below.

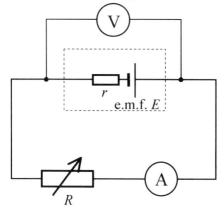

The potential difference and corresponding current are measured as the external resistance is altered by changing the variable resistor. It will be found that as the external resistance decreases and the current increases the reading on the voltmeter will decrease.

(Remember that the circuit is basically two resistors in series and the potential difference will be shared between them. If the external resistance decreases the potential difference across it (the t.p.d.) will decrease. The lost volts will increase as there is more current flowing through the internal resistor than before.)

A graph can be plotted of the potential difference against current.

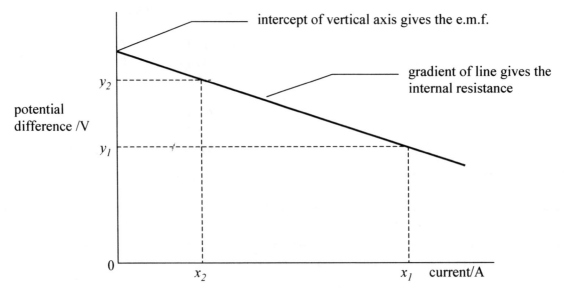

The e.m.f. is measured across the cell when the current flowing is zero so this is given by the intercept of the line on the vertical axis.

The gradient of the graph, $\dfrac{y_2 - y_1}{x_2 - x_1}$, can be used to give the internal resistance of the cell.

The value obtained will be negative due to the slope of the graph so $r = -\text{gradient}$.

If the cell is short-circuited, perhaps by placing a piece of thick wire from one terminal to the other, the only resistance in the circuit will be the internal resistance and the following formula would apply:

$$E.m.f. = I\,r$$

Shorting out a cell is not recommended as the high current which results will cause the cell to overheat.

☑TQ 23 Calculate the e.m.f. and internal resistance of a cell from the graph below.

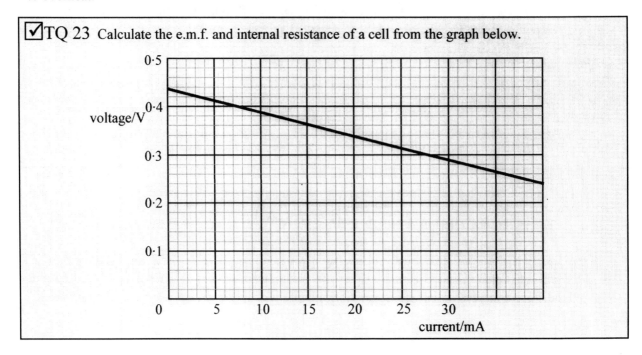

Resistors in Series and Parallel

You will remember using the formula for adding resistors in series and parallel from Standard Grade i.e.

$$R_{TOTAL} = R_1 + R_2 + R_3 \quad \text{for resistors in series}$$

and

$$\frac{1}{R_{TOTAL}} = \frac{1}{R_1} + \frac{1}{R_2} + \frac{1}{R_3} \quad \text{for resistors in parallel}$$

At Higher it is necessary to be able to derive these formulae.

Resistors in Series

Consider the diagram opposite of three resistors in series. By the law of conservation of energy, the sum of the p.d.s across the three resistors must equal the e.m.f. of the cell.

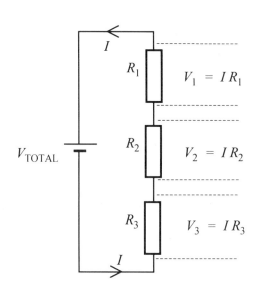

$$V_{TOTAL} = V_1 + V_2 + V_3$$

Since current I flows through all resistors,

$$V_1 = IR_1, \quad V_2 = IR_2, \quad V_3 = IR_3$$

$$IR_{TOTAL} = IR_1 + IR_2 + IR_3$$

$$IR_{TOTAL} = I(R_1 + R_2 + R_3)$$

Cancelling out I gives,

$$R_{TOTAL} = R_1 + R_2 + R_3$$

Resistors in Parallel

Consider three resistors R_1, R_2 and R_3 in parallel. By the law of conservation of charge, the total charge passing through R_1, R_2 and R_3 in one second (the current) must equal the charge in one second (the current) supplied from the cell.

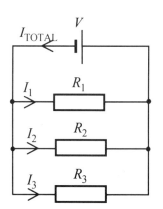

$$I_{TOTAL} = I_1 + I_2 + I_3$$

Since the same potential difference V, is across all resistors,

$$I_1 = \frac{V}{R_1} \quad I_2 = \frac{V}{R_2} \quad I_3 = \frac{V}{R_3}$$

$$\frac{V}{R_{TOTAL}} = \frac{V}{R_1} + \frac{V}{R_2} + \frac{V}{R_3}$$

$$\frac{V}{R_{TOTAL}} = V\left(\frac{1}{R_1} + \frac{1}{R_2} + \frac{1}{R_3}\right)$$

cancelling out V gives

$$\frac{1}{R_{TOTAL}} = \frac{1}{R_1} + \frac{1}{R_2} + \frac{1}{R_3}$$

The two formulae above can be used to solve problems involving any combinations of resistors.

Remember:
- If two resistors of the same value are in parallel, the equivalent resistance is half of the value involved (e.g. two 30 Ω resistors in parallel have an equivalent resistance of 15 Ω).

- If two or more resistors are added in parallel the total resistance will always be less than the value of the smallest resistance present.

Potential Dividers

Problems on potential dividers frequently appear in the Higher examination. There are two ways of solving potential divider problems illustrated below.

Find the potential difference across R_1 in the circuit shown opposite.

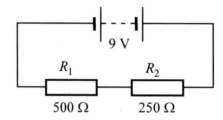

Method 1—By Ratio.

Total resistance = 750 Ω

Potential difference across R_1 is $\dfrac{500}{750}$ of the voltage supply

$$V = \dfrac{500}{750} \times 9$$

$$V = 6 \text{ V}$$

Method 2—By Ohm's Law.

Total resistance = 750 Ω

Total current = $\dfrac{V}{R} = \dfrac{9}{750} = 0\cdot012$ A

Apply Ohm's Law to R_1

$$V = I R_1$$

$$V = 0\cdot012 \times 500$$

$$V = 6 \text{ V}$$

Either of the methods above can be used to find potential differences in a potential divider circuit. Remember the following however:

HINTS:
- The bigger the resistance the bigger will be the potential difference across it.

- The sum of all potential differences must still equal the e.m.f. of the supply.

- If another component such as a resistor or light bulb is placed in parallel with a resistor the potential difference across that resistor will alter as a result—the potential difference must decrease since the total resistance of the combination will decrease.

✓TQ 24 The circuit shown opposite is set up. It consists of two 100 Ω resistors in series. A bulb with a resistance of 50 Ω is placed in parallel with one of the resistors, R_2.

Find the potential difference across the light bulb.

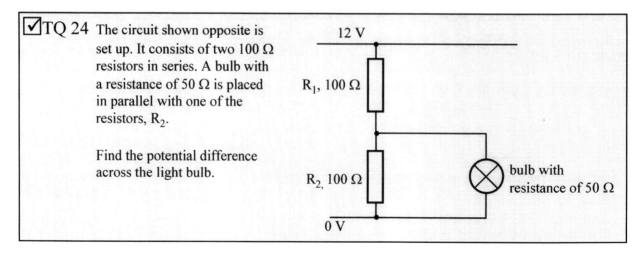

The Wheatstone Bridge

The Wheatstone bridge is a special circuit which can be used to measure resistance. A typical arrangement for such a circuit is shown opposite. It can find resistance more accurately than other methods such as an ammeter-voltmeter method.

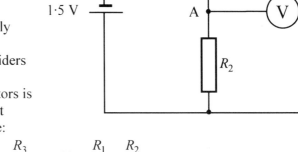

The circuit consists of what is effectively two potential dividers with a voltmeter placed between the middle of these dividers (sometimes an ammeter can be used). Provided the **ratio** of each pair of resistors is the same then the potential difference at points A and B will be the same. Hence:

$$\frac{R_1}{R_2} = \frac{R_3}{R_4} \qquad \text{or} \qquad \frac{R_1}{R_3} = \frac{R_2}{R_4}$$

The bridge is said to be balanced when the potential difference between point A and B is zero i.e. there will be a zero reading on the voltmeter. The above relationship will only hold true when the bridge is balanced.

If the resistance of three of the resistors is known the resistance of the fourth can be calculated. The size of the supply voltage is immaterial and has no effect on the accuracy of the results obtained using this method to measure resistance.

In practice, one of the resistors is usually a **decade resistance box**—this is a device which allows a known resistance to be produced.

☑TQ 25 What must the value of resistor R_X be to produce a balanced bridge?

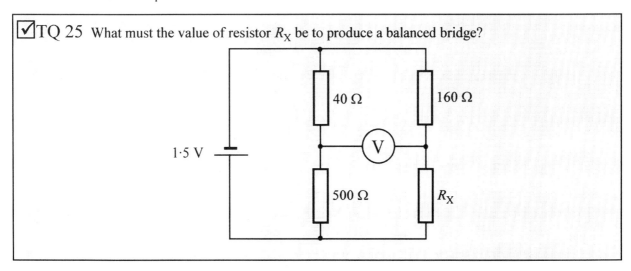

Out of Balance Wheatstone Bridge

A Wheatstone bridge can be used to measure small changes in resistance.

If the resistance of one of the resistors is changed in small steps a graph can be plotted of voltmeter reading against change in resistance. This produces the graph shown below.

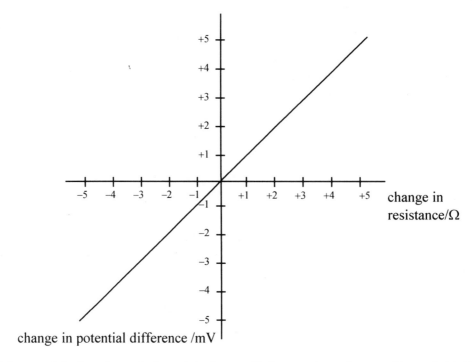

The graph is a straight line through the origin for small changes in resistance. For an initially balanced Wheatstone bridge

$$\Delta V \propto \Delta R.$$

If one of the resistors in a Wheatstone bridge is replaced by a transducer the bridge can be used for making measurements. (A transducer is a component whose resistance varies as a result of changing light level, temperature etc.) Suitable transducers could be strain gauges, light dependent resistors or thermistors.

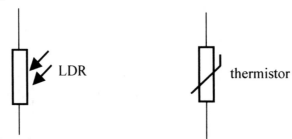

The voltmeter used in the bridge will have to be calibrated i.e. a scale is put on it. In the case of a thermistor its temperature would be altered and the voltmeter reading recorded. A graph of these results would then allow any voltmeter reading to be converted into the corresponding temperature.

Alternating Current and Voltage

A.C.

Alternating current is delivered by the mains at 230 V, 50 Hz. An oscilloscope can be used to measure the frequency of an a.c. supply. To find the frequency of a wave its period (the time for one complete wave) must first be found from the oscilloscope. The frequency can then be calculated using the formula ;

$$\text{frequency} = \frac{1}{\text{period}} \qquad f = \frac{1}{T} \qquad \text{where } f = \text{frequency measured in hertz (Hz)}$$
$$T = \text{period measured in seconds (s)}$$

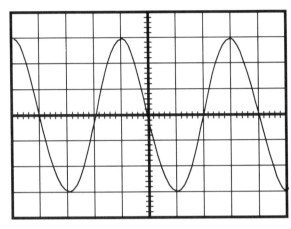

timebase set at 5 ms per division

The oscilloscope screen shown opposite has its timebase set at 5 milliseconds per division. Since each wave covers five divisions the period of the wave is 20 milliseconds. This gives a frequency of 50 Hz.

Peak and r.m.s. Voltage

At Standard Grade you were taught that an a.c. voltage had a maximum, peak value and also a quoted value which was lower. At Higher the reason for these two values is examined more closely.

The peak voltage is the maximum reached by the supply and is easily read from the oscilloscope screen. In the example shown opposite the Y gain is set at 10 V per division giving a peak voltage of 36 V.

The r.m.s. value of an a.c. supply cannot be measured directly from the oscilloscope but must be calculated. It is defined as being the value of an a.c. voltage which will deliver the same amount of energy as a d.c. voltage.

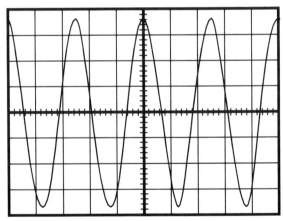

Y gain set at 10 V per division

Peak and r.m.s. voltage are related by the following formulae:

$$V_{peak} = V_{rms} \times \sqrt{2} \qquad \text{and} \qquad V_{rms} = \frac{V_{peak}}{\sqrt{2}}$$

Peak and r.m.s. current can be measured in exactly the same way:

$$I_{peak} = I_{rms} \times \sqrt{2} \qquad \text{and} \qquad I_{rms} = \frac{I_{peak}}{\sqrt{2}}$$

☑TQ 26   A power supply producing a peak voltage of 16 V is connected to a 30 Ω resistor.

   (a) What will be the V_{rms} produced by the power supply?

   (b) What will be the value of I_{peak} and I_{rms} in the circuit?

Note:
- If an oscilloscope is used to measure voltage then it will be the peak value which is being measured. Digital multimeters or moving coil meters measure the r.m.s. value of voltage.

- The peak values are measured from the centre line of an oscilloscope.

- If one wishes to make a direct comparison between an a.c. supply and a d.c. supply it is the V_{rms} which delivers the same energy as the d.c. source i.e. $V_{rms} \Leftrightarrow V_{dc}$.

- V_{peak} will always be a larger value than its equivalent V_{rms}.

Current and Frequency in a Resistive Circuit
A variable frequency a.c. supply can be connected to a circuit containing a resistor and the supply frequency altered.

The supply voltage is kept constant (checked using the voltmeter) and a graph plotted of current against frequency.

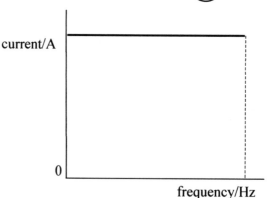

There is no change in the current flowing in the circuit as the frequency is altered i.e. current is independent of frequency in a resistive circuit.

Capacitance

Capacitance
Capacitors are components first met in the Electronics section of Standard Grade Physics. They were used as input devices and to provide a time delay in electronic circuits. Capacitors are able to store an electric charge and consist of two foil plates separated by an insulating layer.

The symbol for a capacitor is:

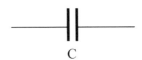

When a cell or battery is connected to a capacitor, electrons flow from the negative terminal on to one of the plates. The electrons cannot cross the insulating layer but are attracted from the other plate to the positive terminal of the cell leaving it positive.

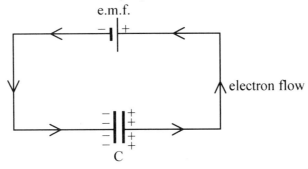

In this way a flow of electrons is maintained around the circuit until the potential difference across the plates is the same as the e.m.f. of the cell. When this stage has been reached it is not possible for any more electrons to move on to the plate of the capacitor and current ceases to flow in the circuit. The capacitor is now fully charged.

The capacitor's ability to store charge is known as its **capacitance** and is measured in **farads**. The farad is a rather large unit so practical capacitors are measured in much smaller units, usually micro-farads or nano-farads.

$1 \text{ F} = 1\ 000\ 000 \ \mu\text{F}$ (micro farad)   so $1 \ \mu\text{F} = 1 \times 10^{-6} \text{ F}$

$1 \text{ F} = 1\ 000\ 000\ 000 \text{ nF}$ (nano farad)   so $1 \text{ nF} = 1 \times 10^{-9} \text{ F}$

$1 \text{ F} = 1\ 000\ 000\ 000\ 000 \text{ pF}$ (pico farad)   so $1 \text{ pF} = 1 \times 10^{-12} \text{ F}$

Charge and Potential Difference Across a Capacitor
An experiment can be carried out to investigate the relationship between the potential difference across a capacitor and the charge stored on it. To do this the circuit shown below is used.

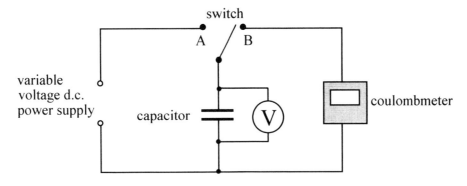

With the switch connected to position A the capacitor is allowed to fully charge and the voltage on the voltmeter is recorded.

The switch is then moved to position B which disconnects it from the power supply and connects it to a coulombmeter. The capacitor discharges into the coulombmeter which measures directly the charge which was stored by the capacitor.

The experiment is repeated over a range of supply voltages and a graph of charge against potential difference across the capacitor drawn.

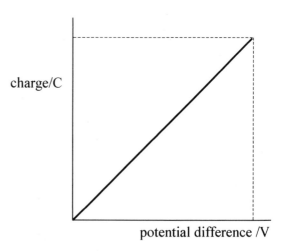

charge/C

potential difference /V

The graph produced is a straight line through the origin indicating that charge and potential difference are directly proportional. The gradient of the graph will give a constant which is the capacitance of the capacitor. Hence:

$$\text{capacitance} = \frac{\text{charge}}{\text{potential difference}} \qquad C = \frac{Q}{V}$$

capacitance in farads (F)
charge in coulombs (C)
potential difference in volts (V)

This formula can be remembered as $Q = VC$ (the *Q*ueen gives out the *V*ictoria *C*ross!)

Confusion sometimes arises over the units and symbols in this section.

- The symbol for capacitance is C and the unit the farad, F.

- The symbol for charge is Q and the unit the coulomb, C.

☑TQ 27   A 2200 μF capacitor is connected to a 12 V power supply. What will be the charge on the plates of the capacitor when it is fully charged?

Energy Stored on a Capacitor
When an uncharged capacitor is connected to a cell or other power supply electrons flow on to the negative plate of the capacitor.

The negative charge which builds up on one plate will produce an electrostatic force which will make it more difficult for 'following' electrons to move on to the plate.

In order to move charges on to the plate the cell must do work against this force.

The charge builds up on the plates, negative charge on one plate and positive on the other. As a result there is a potential difference across the plates which is acting in the opposite direction to the potential difference of the cell. When the potential difference across the capacitor and the e.m.f. of the cell are the same then current ceases to flow and the capacitor is fully charged.

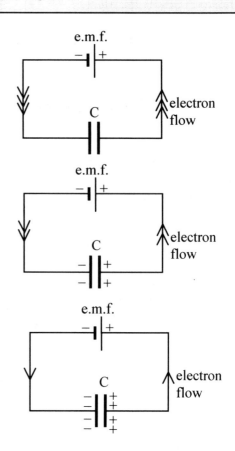

The work required to put the charge on to the capacitor will be equivalent to the energy stored on the capacitor. The general formula for work done is work done = charge × potential difference across capacitor, $W = QV$. However, the potential difference across a capacitor varies but it is possible to calculate the energy stored from the area under the charge-potential difference graph.

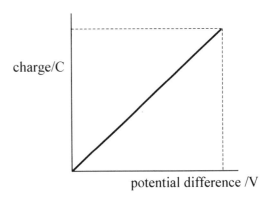

charge/C

potential difference /V

The area under the graph is equivalent to ½ × Q × V. Thus:

energy stored on a capacitor = ½ × charge × potential difference $E = ½QV$

E = energy stored in joules (J)
Q = charge on capacitor in coulombs (C)
V = potential difference across capacitor in volts (V)

The energy stored by the capacitor (½QV) is exactly half the work done by the cell. The other half of the energy is mainly converted into heat energy in the resistance of the circuit during the rush of electrons on to one plate and off the other.

Equations for energy stored on a capacitor

By using the formula $C = \dfrac{Q}{V}$ and combining it with $E = ½QV$ it is possible to obtain two other equations.

$$E = ½QV$$
$$\sin ce\ Q = CV$$
$$E = ½CV \times V$$
$$so\ E = ½CV^2$$

$$E = ½QV$$
$$\sin ce\ V = \frac{Q}{C}$$
$$E = ½Q \times \frac{Q}{C}$$
$$so\ E = ½\frac{Q^2}{C}$$

This now gives three equations for the energy stored on a capacitor.

$$E = ½QV \qquad E = ½CV^2 \qquad E = ½\frac{Q^2}{C}$$

The formula $Q = It$ may also be used along with capacitance questions to calculate the charge flowing on to the capacitor providing the charging current is kept constant.

☑TQ 28   A capacitor with a value of 1000 µF stores 400 mJ of energy.

(a)   What will be the potential difference across the capacitor?

(b)   How much charge is being stored by the capacitor?

Graphs of Charging and Discharging of a Capacitor
Graphs can be plotted for current against time and potential difference against time for a charging and discharging capacitor. A typical circuit used to obtain these is shown below.

The position of the two-way switch can be altered to either charge or discharge the capacitor.

An oscilloscope placed across the capacitor can be used to indicate the potential difference across the capacitor.

A second oscilloscope is placed across the resistor to indicate the current flowing in the circuit since the potential difference across the resistor will be proportional to current.

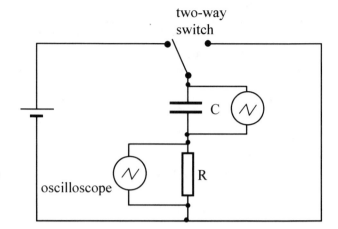

Graphs for a charging capacitor

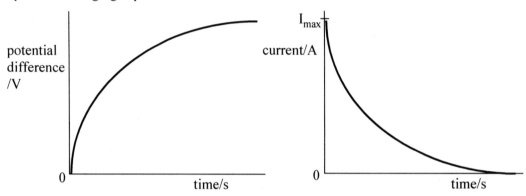

Graphs for a discharging capacitor

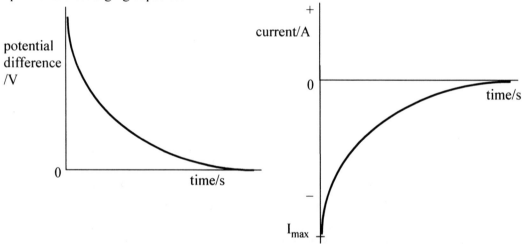

Note:
- The discharge current is in the opposite direction to the charging current—the electrons are flowing on to the negative plate during charging and flowing off the negative plate during discharging.

- The charging and discharging current always ends at 0 A.

- The capacitor always charges up to the supply voltage and on discharging reaches 0 V (assuming there is sufficient time for this to take place).

- The initial current when charging depends upon the supply voltage and the resistance in the circuit.

$$I_{maximum} = \frac{V_{supply}}{R}$$

- The initial current when discharging depends upon the potential difference across the capacitor and the resistance in the circuit.

$$I_{maximum} = \frac{V_{capacitor}}{R}$$

- If the capacitance of the capacitor in a circuit is increased (and all other values remain the same) the capacitor will take longer to charge or discharge. This is because it will be storing more charge although the final potential difference across the capacitor will be the same.

- If there is a resistor in series with a capacitor and the value of this is increased (and all other values remain the same) the capacitor will take longer to charge or discharge. The amount of charge stored will be the same but it takes longer to flow on to or off the capacitor because the current is smaller. Once again the final voltage reached will be the same.

☑TQ 29   A 2200 µF capacitor is connected in series with a 1 kΩ resistor. The capacitor is initially discharged when the switch, S, is closed and the capacitor is allowed to charge.

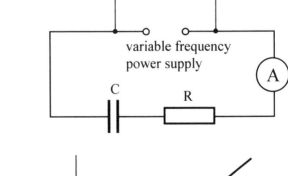

   (a)   Sketch a graph of potential difference across the capacitor against time (numerical values on the axis are not required).

   (b)   Calculate the initial charging current in the circuit.

   (c)   Calculate the energy stored on the capacitor when it is fully charged.

Current and Frequency in a Capacitive Circuit
A variable frequency a.c. supply can be connected to a circuit containing a capacitor and the supply frequency altered. The voltmeter is used to ensure the supply voltage remains constant and a graph is plotted of current against frequency.

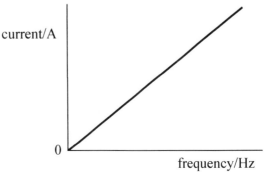

The graph indicates that for a circuit containing a capacitor the current flowing will be directly proportional to the frequency of the supply.

$$I \propto f_{supply}$$

Capacitors oppose low frequency and allow through high frequencies. At low frequencies the capacitor becomes fully charged and blocks the current for much of the time. At high frequencies the capacitor never has time to become fully charged before the supply direction reverses and so current is always flowing.

Uses of Capacitors
Capacitors have a range of uses including:

* Storing energy for devices such as a camera flashgun.

* Power supplies which convert a.c. to d.c. use capacitors to store charge and release this to smooth out any ripples in the supply voltage.

* Capacitors can be used to block d.c. signals and allow a.c. (high frequency) signals through.

Analogue Electronics

The Op-amp
This section is concerned with the study of operational amplifiers—called op-amps for short. The op-amp takes an input voltage and produces a copy of it at the output, usually with a larger amplitude. The amount by which the amplitude of the signal is altered is controlled by components placed around the op-amp. Shown below is a typical op-amp circuit.

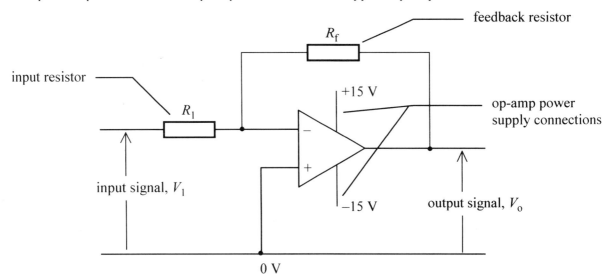

There are two inputs into the op-amp, the **inverting input** and the **non-inverting input**.

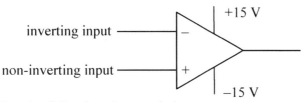

An ideal op-amp has the following characteristics:

- The input resistance to the op-amp is infinite and so no current can flow into its inputs.

- Both the inverting and non-inverting inputs will be at the same potential. In the diagram below the non-inverting input is connected to 0 V so both inputs must be at 0 V.

The Inverting Mode
The op-amp in the diagram at the top of this page is connected in inverting mode. i.e. the input signal is fed into the inverting input. An op-amp is a voltage amplifier and so the input would take the form of a potential difference between the input and ground line or 0 V.

Note:
- The output signal is the opposite sign to the input signal i.e. the output is inverted.

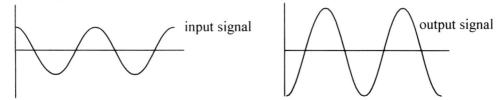

- Resistors R_1 and R_f are used to control the amplification of the amplifier.

- The power supply to the op-amp is typically +15 V and −15 V. Both voltages are required since the op-amp must produce a positive and negative output. Sometimes these are omitted from diagrams.

The Gain Equation
The amount of amplification which an op-amp provides is called its gain. The amount of gain an amplifier will produce depends upon the value of the resistors R_1 and R_f. This is given by the equation below.

$$\text{gain} = \frac{V_o}{V_1} = -\frac{R_f}{R_1}$$

V_o = output voltage in volts (V)
V_1 = input voltage in volts (V)
R_f = feedback resistor in ohms (Ω)
R_1 = input resistor in ohms (Ω)

☑TQ 30   An op-amp is connected as shown below.

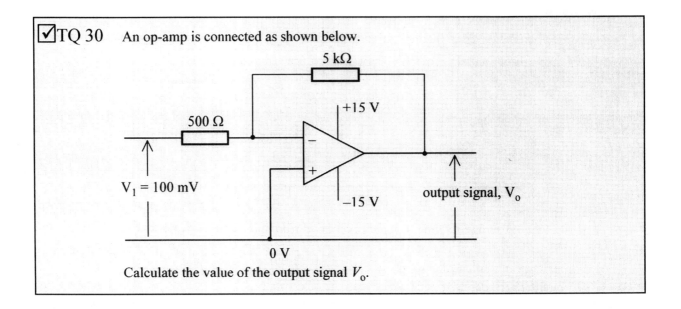

Calculate the value of the output signal V_o.

Adding Signals
It is possible for an op-amp to be used to add signals together by using two or more inputs into the inverting input. The circuit shown below will add together two signals, the gain equation being applied to each input separately and the two outputs being added together.

Example:

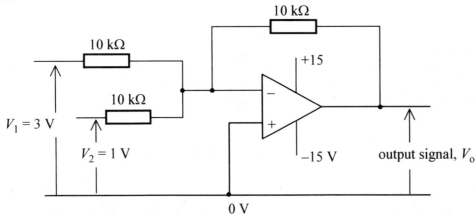

The gain for input V_1 is –1 and the gain for V_2 is –1. Both inputs are added together to give a total output voltage V_o of –4 V.

In effect, this circuit is carrying out the arithmetical operation of addition. There may be more than two inputs but the same rules will apply as in the example above. If one of the inputs is made negative it is then possible to get the circuit to subtract one value from the other.

Saturation

It is important to realise that the output voltage from an op-amp is not the input voltage somehow altered to be bigger as happens in a transformer. It is much easier to think of an op-amp as a control circuit where it produces an output voltage and the size of this is controlled by the value of the input and feedback resistors and the value of the input voltage.

The energy for the output voltage comes from the op-amp power supply and as such, it is impossible for the output to exceed the power supply voltage.

Most op-amps have a 12 V or 15 V power supply which provides both positive and negative voltages at these values. In practice the output from the op-amp would only be about 85% of the power supply value so the maximum obtainable will be slightly less.

In the circuit below the op-amp has a gain of –200.

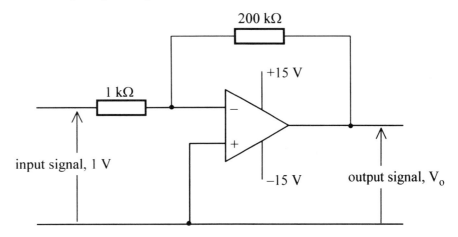

If the input signal is 1 V this should, in theory, produce an output of –200 V (remember the signal is inverted). In practice the output voltage will not exceed –13 V. The output is said to be in **saturation** since no matter how much bigger the input gets the output will remain constant.

The graph opposite illustrates this. As the positive input voltage is increased the output gets more and more negative until it reaches the power supply voltage. The output then remains at this value no matter how much the input is increased.

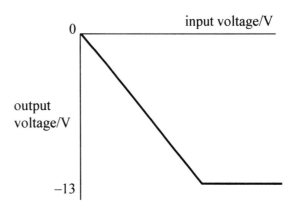

Producing Square Waves

The property of saturation can be made use of to produce square waves from a sinusoidal wave input.

On the right is shown an input signal to an op-amp. This signal is fed into an op-amp with a gain such that it causes saturation.

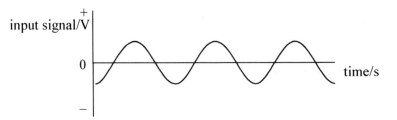

The output signal from the op-amp is shown here. The output signal increases up to a certain point then remains constant. The troughs and crests are cut off (clipped).

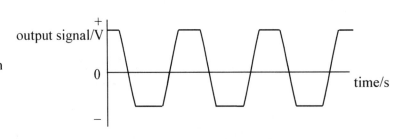

If the gain is increased even further the result is an output signal which is practically a pure square wave.

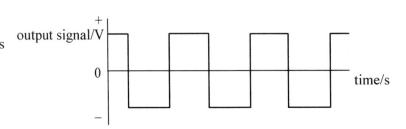

Differential Mode

In the differential mode both the inverting and non-inverting inputs are used. A typical circuit is shown below.

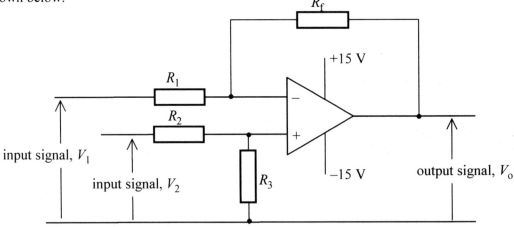

In this mode both inputs are used. The amplifier amplifies **the potential difference between the two signals at the inputs**. The gain applied to this potential difference is still calculated by the ratio of feedback to input resistor.

To calculate the output voltage the following formula is used:

$$V_o = (V_2 - V_1)\frac{R_f}{R_1}$$

The ratio of R_f to R_1 determines the gain of V_1 whilst the ratio of R_3 to R_2 determines the gain of V_2. These two ratios will always be the same.

A problem can arise over determining whether V_o is positive or negative. If you remember that input V_1 is to the inverting input and V_2 to the non-inverting input then the correct answer will be arrived at using the formula above. A second simple method is to remember that if the input to the inverting input is bigger the output is negative and if the input to the non-inverting input is bigger the output will be positive.

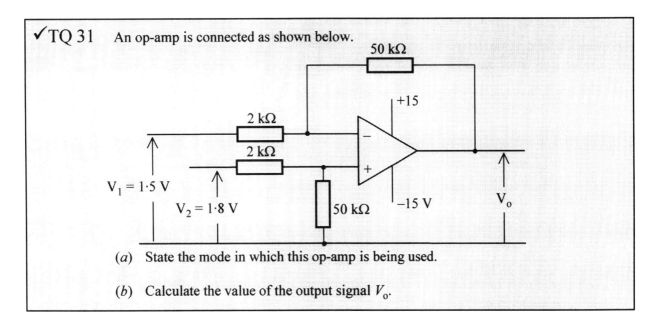

✓TQ 31   An op-amp is connected as shown below.

(a)   State the mode in which this op-amp is being used.

(b)   Calculate the value of the output signal V_o.

The Differential Amplifier and the Wheatstone Bridge
The Wheatstone bridge can be used to measure small changes in factors such as light levels, temperature etc. by replacing one resistor in the bridge with a suitable transducer (light dependent resistor, thermistor). The output from the bridge circuit is very small so can be amplified using an op-amp circuit.

The circuit shown below can be used to monitor temperature.

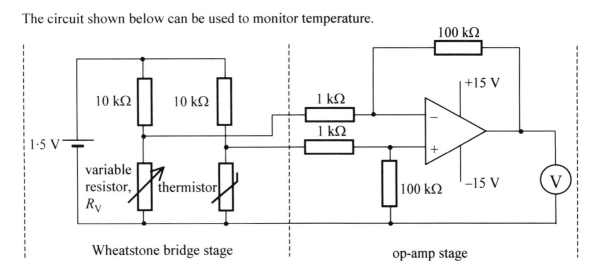

Wheatstone bridge stage   op-amp stage

The potential difference across a balanced bridge is 0 V. Thus if the bridge is initially balanced then both inputs to the op-amp will be at same voltage. Any change in temperature will cause a change in resistance of the thermistor and throw the bridge out of balance. There will now be a potential difference between the inputs of the op-amp which will be amplified by the appropriate gain factor.

Devices such as the one above must be **calibrated** i.e. the output voltage must be measured and related to the corresponding temperature of the thermistor. Once this has been done a graph of thermistor temperature against voltage output can be plotted allowing the temperature to be found from any voltage output.

Using the Op-amp for Control

Since the circuit shown above can be used for monitoring it would be useful if the op-amp could also be used for control, perhaps for switching on and off heaters or lights. Unfortunately it is a device which cannot supply more than a few milliamperes of current so an additional output device must be used. This is often a transistor as shown in the circuit below.

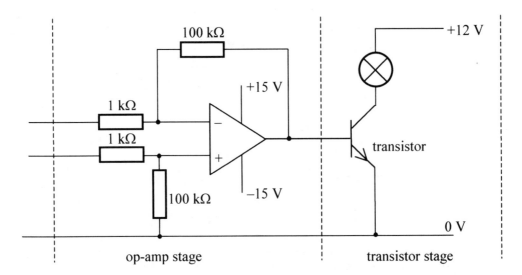

Whenever there is a positive output from the op-amp the transistor will be switched on and the lamp will light. The lamp does not draw any current directly from the op-amp.

UNIT 3 Radiation and Matter

Waves

Wave Characteristics

Several topics in Standard Grade provided information on the behaviour of waves. This can be collected together and is summarised below.

Waves are responsible for the transmission of energy. Some examples of waves are sound waves, the electromagnetic spectrum (of which light is a part) and water waves. All waves show certain properties which include:

reflection—occurs when waves bounce off a surface obeying the law of reflection i.e. angle of incidence is equal to the angle of reflection. There is no change in the wave speed, wavelength or frequency of the wave when reflection occurs.

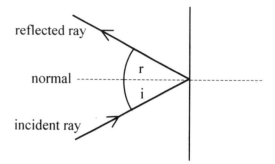

refraction—occurs when waves travel from one medium to another. This may cause the waves to change the direction of their travel. When waves refract, the wavelength and speed of the waves changes, but the frequency remains fixed.

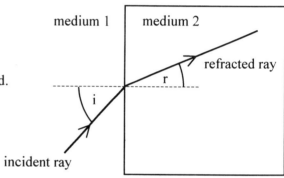

In the example opposite the waves bends towards the normal as it travels from the less dense medium 1 into the more dense medium 2.

diffraction—diffraction is the effect observed when waves bend around an obstacle, such as the bending of radio waves around a hillside. Long wavelengths diffract or bend more than short wavelengths. There is no change in the speed, wavelength or frequency of the wave when diffraction occurs.

Wave definitions

Wavelength λ—the wavelength of a wave is the minimum distance in which a wave repeats and is measured in metres (m) e.g. the distance between two consecutive crests or troughs.

Amplitude—the amplitude of a wave is the maximum displacement of the wave from its rest position, also measured in metres (m). The amplitude of a wave is determined by the energy it carries.

Frequency f—the frequency is the number of complete vibrations or cycles each second and is measured in hertz (Hz).

Time period T—the time period (often called the period) is the time taken for one complete vibration to be produced or the time for a complete wave to pass a point and is measure in seconds (s).

Frequency and period are related by the equation

$$\text{frequency} = \frac{1}{\text{period}}, \quad f = \frac{1}{T}$$

$$\text{or} \quad T = \frac{1}{f}$$

Frequency in hertz, (Hz)
Period in seconds (s)

You should also remember the previously learned wave equation

$$\text{wave speed} = \text{frequency x wavelength}, \quad v = f \times \lambda$$

Wave speed in metres per second (m s^{-1})
Frequency in hertz, (Hz)
Wavelength in metres (m)

☑TQ 32 A tuning fork vibrates with a frequency of 500 Hz. Calculate the period of the sound wave produced.

Interference of Waves
When the paths of two or more waves cross, the waves pass through each other and continue with their original shape. At the point where they cross however, they add together or superimpose to produce a disturbance which is the sum of all the waves arriving at that point.

Interference can be observed when two waves with the same frequency and wavelength and travelling at the same speed overlap. The effect produced will be dependent upon whether these waves are **in phase** or **out of phase**.

In Phase Waves
wave 1
wave 2

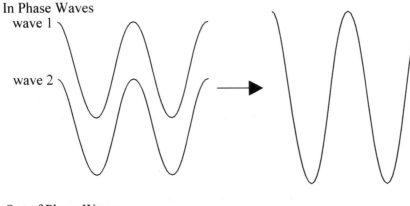

Two waves of equal amplitude meeting in phase will combine to give a wave of twice the amplitude.

This is called **constructive interference**.

Out of Phase Waves

wave 1
wave 2

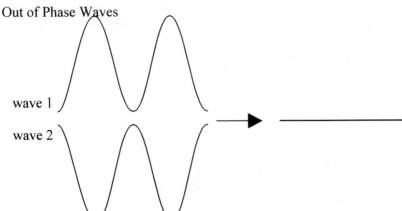

Two waves of equal amplitude meeting out of phase will combine to give a wave of zero amplitude.

This is called **destructive interference**.

Constructive interference can be defined as waves from two sources arriving at the same point **in phase** so causing an increase in amplitude. It can also be described as a wave crest coinciding with a wave crest or a wave trough coinciding with a wave trough.

Destructive interference can be defined as waves from two sources arriving **out of phase** so causing a cancelling out of the wave. It can also be described as a wave crest coinciding with a wave trough.

To prove that energy is being transferred **by a wave** it is only necessary to demonstrate interference as the other wave properties such as diffraction, reflection and refraction are not conclusive proof that a wave is present.

Experiments on Interference
There are a number of common experiments performed at school level which demonstrate interference and exam questions are often based on these. A good understanding of these experiments is necessary to answer them successfully.

Interference of Light Using a Double Slit
Interference of light using a double slit (Young's double slit experiment) is commonly used to demonstrate interference of light. To produce interference it is necessary to have two sources of light which are **coherent**. Waves which are coherent have the same frequency, wavelength and velocity and have a constant phase relationship. For our purposes, this means that the two sources of waves are exactly the same and both sets of waves are in phase at the source.

Coherent light sources are produced when light from a bulb passes through a single slit followed by a double slit. Monochromatic light is used i.e. light which contains only one wavelength such as a sodium lamp.

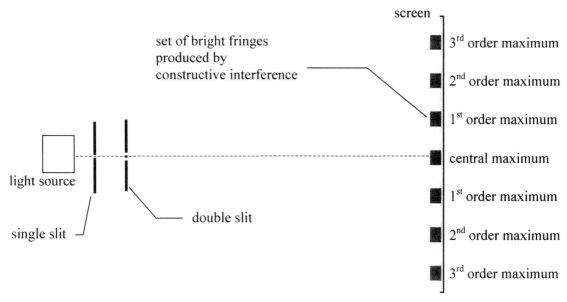

The effect seen on the screen is of a series of light and dark bands. The light areas are where constructive interference occurs and the dark bands are found where destructive interference takes place.

A view looking down on the waves produces the diagram below. The solid lines represent wave crests with the wave troughs in between. Note the diagram is not to scale.

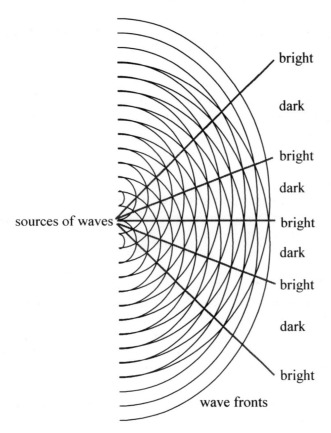

Lines have been drawn through the points where constructive interference occurs (where crest meets crest and trough meets trough) and a screen placed in front of this would give the characteristic pattern of bright fringes.

Sound Waves and Interference
As sound is a wave it can be used to produce interference. It is especially good at demonstrating the role of **path difference** in interference.

Consider sound waves being produced by two loudspeakers connected to the same source so that they are producing sound which is coherent.

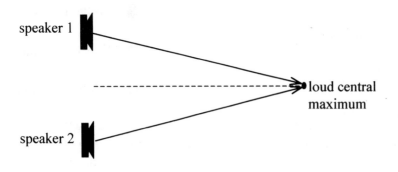

The path from each speaker to the central maximum is the same—there is no path difference. If the waves were coherent and produced in phase they will still be in phase when they coincide so giving constructive interference.

In this next diagram the path to the 1st order maximum can be examined where constructive interference can also be found. The extra distance between the 1st order maximum and speaker 2 is one wavelength (1 λ) more than from the 1st order maximum to speaker 1 i.e. there is a path difference of one wavelength.

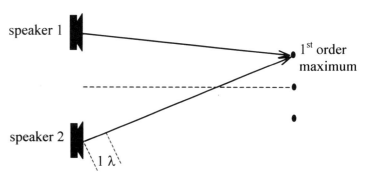

If one of the waves has to travel a whole wavelength more or a multiple of whole wavelengths more, the waves arrive in phase and produce constructive interference.

The example below shows destructive interference:

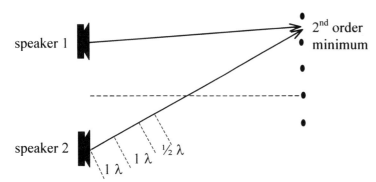

A path difference of a whole number of wavelengths and a half gives destructive interference. In this case a crest and trough coincide to produce a minimum between the 2nd and 3rd order maximum.

The effect of path difference is summarised in the following rule:

path difference $= n\lambda$ for a maximum (constructive interference)

path difference $= (n + \frac{1}{2})\lambda$ for a minimum (destructive interference)

where n is an integer.

☑TQ 33 Two sources of coherent water waves meet to produce interference. The distance travelled by one wave is 65 cm and the distance travelled by the other is 85 cm. What type of interference will occur if the waves have a wavelength of 10 cm?

Interference of Microwaves
Microwaves have a wavelength of about 3 cm and can also be used to show interference. A typical experiment is shown below.

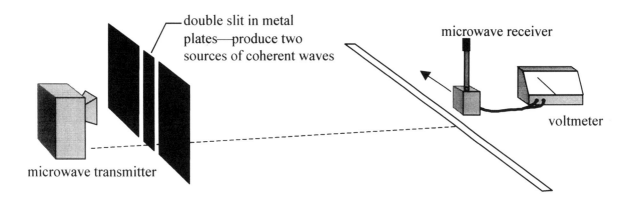

The same rules apply as to other forms of interference. Microwaves can also be used to demonstrate interference with a single source of waves, a reflector being used to produce a second reflected wave and give interference.

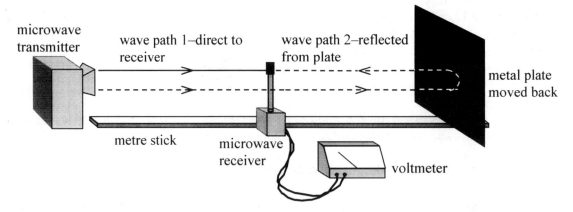

The wave which is reflected has to travel a greater distance than the wave reaching the receiver directly. If this extra distance—the path difference—is equivalent to a whole number of wavelengths then constructive interference will occur at the receiver. If the reflected path is a whole number of wavelengths and a half greater, then destructive interference occurs.

Moving the metal plate backwards or forwards will change this path difference. If the receiver is placed at a point of constructive interference then the plate only has to be moved back half a wavelength to obtain constructive interference again. Remember that the wave has to travel this extra distance to the plate and back again—moving it back 1·5 cm will introduce an extra path difference of 3·0 cm.

☑TQ 34 A microwave source produces microwaves with a wavelength of 4 cm. The source is directed at a detector behind which sits a metal plate. The microwaves are reflected by the metal plate back to the detector to produce constructive interference, indicated by a high reading on the voltmeter.

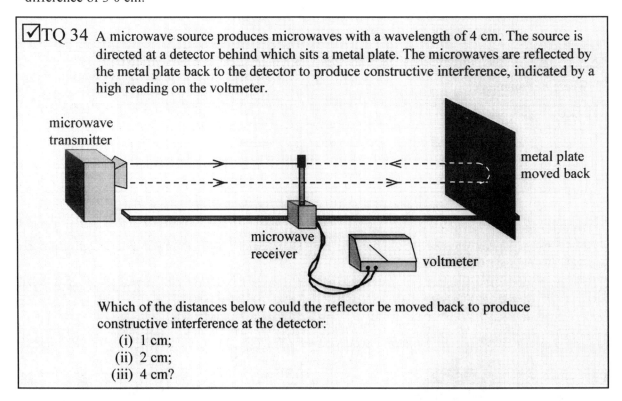

Which of the distances below could the reflector be moved back to produce constructive interference at the detector:
    (i)   1 cm;
    (ii) 2 cm;
    (iii) 4 cm?

Colour and Wavelength of Light

You should know the approximate wavelength of light in the visible spectrum. This wavelength is commonly quoted in nanometres (nm), 1 nm being equivalent to 1×10^{-9} m.

red light	700 nm	$7\cdot0 \times 10^{-7}$ m
green light	550 nm	$5\cdot5 \times 10^{-7}$ m
violet light	400 nm	$4\cdot0 \times 10^{-7}$ m

The Diffraction Grating

A diffraction grating is made up of many slits placed very close together. Light passes through these, and as a result of the path difference to the screen, an interference pattern is produced similar to that for a double slit but:

- the fringes produced are much brighter;

- the fringes are much sharper.

Diffraction gratings can be used with monochromatic light sources or with white light. They can also be used with a laser to produce especially clear fringes and the set up for this experiment is shown below.

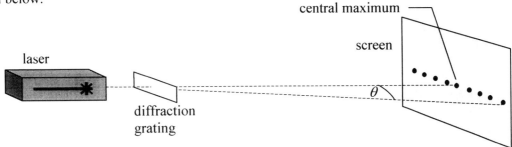

The light from the laser is diffracted through the numerous small slits in the grating (hence the name) so that the light overlaps. The bright spots of light on the screen are produced due to constructive interference. The centre fringe is called the central maximum or zero order fringe. The next fringes on either side are the first order fringe and the next the second order fringe and so on.

A formula which relates the wavelength of incident light, the order of the fringe and the angle of deviation θ is;

$$n\lambda = d\sin\theta$$

n = order of fringe
λ = wavelength of light in metres (m)
d = distance between slits of grating in metres (m)
θ = angle of deviation between central maxima and order of fringe being considered in degrees

Example: A diffraction grating with 500 lines per millimetre is illuminated with a laser in such a way that a second order maximum is obtained at an angle of deviation of 22°. Calculate the wavelength of the light used.

Answer: The distance between slits, d, must first be calculated. Note that the question gives the numbers of lines on the grating NOT the distance between them—this is very common in grating questions. (i.e. $d = \dfrac{1}{\text{number of lines per metre}}$)

$$n\lambda = d\sin\theta$$
$$2 \times \lambda = 2 \times 10^{-6} \times \sin 22°$$
$$\lambda = \frac{2 \times 10^{-6} \times 0\cdot375}{2}$$
$$\lambda = \frac{7\cdot49 \times 10^{-7}}{2}$$
$$\lambda = 3\cdot75 \times 10^{-7} \text{ m}$$

500 lines per mm = 500×1000 lines in 1 m

$$d = \frac{1}{500\,000}$$
$$d = 2 \times 10^{-6} \text{ m}$$

Diffraction Gratings and White Light

If white light is used the pattern seen on the screen is quite different as the different wavelengths of light making up white light all have their interference maxima at slightly different positions. A white central maxima is produced with coloured spectra positioned at either side of this as shown below.

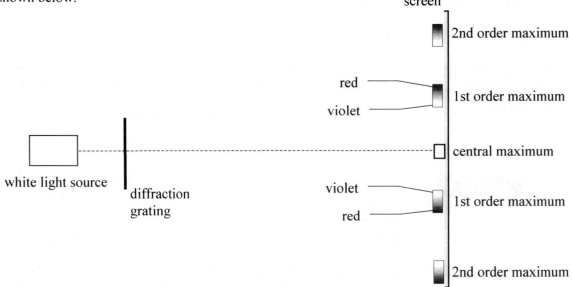

NOTE:

* The central maximum is always white since the path difference to this point is zero for all wavelengths so they all have their maximum at the same point, recombining to give white light.

* The outer maxima are spectra, differing wavelengths producing a path difference of a whole number of wavelengths at slightly different positions.

* Red is always to the outside and violet to the inside since red has the longest wavelength. Other colours are in between.

* A number of spectra are produced but these get less bright and more spread out as you move further from the centre.

Diffraction Gratings and Prisms

Both diffraction gratings and prisms can be used to produce a spectrum from white light.
The differences between the spectrums produced by these methods are as follows.

Diffraction Grating	Prism
Produces many spectra	Produces only one spectrum
Spectra are produced by interference of light	Spectra are produced by refraction of light
Red light is deviated most	Red light is deviated least
Spectra are bright	The spectrum is dim

☑TQ 35 A white light source is viewed through a diffraction grating of 1000 lines per centimetre. Part of the 1st order fringe makes an angle of deviation of 4·0°. What colour of light would be found at this point?

Refraction of Light

When light travels from one medium to another, such as from air to glass, it is said to be refracted. If the ray of light enters a more dense material at an angle the ray will be bent towards the normal. If it enters a less dense material it bends away from the normal.

The amount of bending that a ray of light undergoes depends upon:

- the wavelength or frequency of the light being used;

- the type of material into which the ray passes.

Different materials are said to have a different **refractive index** i.e. a number or index indicating that material's ability to bend light.

If a light ray travels from air to glass the relationship between the angle of incidence and angle of refraction is as stated below.

$$\text{refractive index, } n = \frac{\sin \theta_{air}}{\sin \theta_{glass}}$$

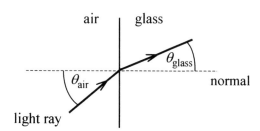

Since n is an index it has no units and is only a number.

NOTE:
- The refractive index of a material is always greater than 1.

- To calculate the refractive index of a material divide $\sin \theta_{air}$ by $\sin \theta_{material}$ whether the light goes from air into the material or the opposite direction.

- If white light is used (say in a prism) the shorter wavelengths (blue) are refracted more than long wavelengths (red).

- The **frequency** of light **does not** alter on being refracted, only the wave speed and wavelength are altered.

Example: A ray of light passes out of a glass block as shown opposite.
Calculate the refractive index of the glass.

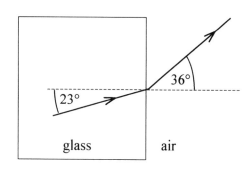

Answer: refractive index, $n = \dfrac{\sin \theta_{air}}{\sin \theta_{glass}}$

$$n = \frac{\sin 36°}{\sin 23°}$$

$$n = 1\cdot 5$$

☑TQ 36 Calculate the refractive index of the glass block shown opposite.

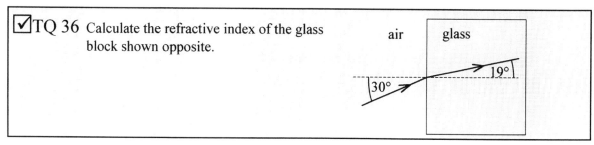

Measuring the Refractive Index of a Material

An experiment can be performed to measure the refractive index of a glass or perspex block using the arrangement shown opposite.

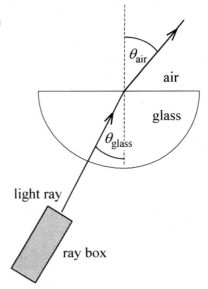

The ray of light is shone into the centre of a semicircular block as shown. The ray does not bend on entering the block as it passes along the normal but on emerging from the block it is refracted away from the normal. The angles in air and the medium are measured.

The refractive index can be calculated using the relationship $n = \dfrac{\sin \theta_{air}}{\sin \theta_{glass}}$, n being a constant.

A graph of $\sin \theta_{air}$ against $\sin \theta_{glass}$ can also be plotted which will produce a straight line through the origin.

Other Refractive Index Formulae

Apart from the formula already covered there are other formulae which can be used to find the refractive index of a material. It has been stated that the wavelength and wave speed alter as a wave passes from one medium to another. As a result the ratio of these properties can also be used to find the refractive index. Hence,

refractive index, $n = \dfrac{\sin \theta_{air}}{\sin \theta_{medium}}$ or $\dfrac{\text{wave speed in air}}{\text{wave speed in medium}}$ or $\dfrac{\text{wavelength in air}}{\text{wavelength in medium}}$

$$n = \dfrac{\sin \theta_{air}}{\sin \theta_{medium}}, \qquad n = \dfrac{v_{air}}{v_{medium}}, \qquad n = \dfrac{\lambda_{air}}{\lambda_{medium}}$$

☑TQ 37 Light approaches a glass block at 3×10^8 m s^{-1} and upon entering the block its speed is reduced to 2×10^8 m s^{-1}. If the wavelength of the light is 600 nm in air, find its wavelength in the glass block.

Total Internal Reflection

The principle of total internal reflection featured in Standard Grade Telecommunications and Health Physics when the way in which light is transmitted down optic fibres was examined.

It is now possible to relate this property to the refractive index of a material. Consider the diagram opposite. If the angle of incidence in the glass block is increased it is possible to achieve an angle in the air of 90°.
The incident ray is then said to be at the critical angle, often referred to as θ_c.

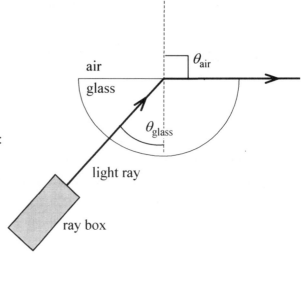

Applying the formula for refractive index gives:

$$\text{refractive index, } n = \dfrac{\sin \theta_{air}}{\sin \theta_{glass}}$$

$$n = \dfrac{\sin 90°}{\sin \theta_c}$$

$$n = \dfrac{1}{\sin \theta_c}$$

This gives a fourth formula for use with refractive index namely $n = \dfrac{1}{\sin \theta_c}$.

Total internal reflection can occur whenever light passes from an optically dense medium to a less dense medium e.g. glass to air or water to air. It should be noted that some light is reflected back when the ray is below the critical angle but that **total** internal reflection occurs when the incident light is above θ_c.

The critical angle can be measured experimentally by using a semicircular glass block and a ray box as shown in the diagram above. When the light ray emerges along the face of the glass block the angle of the incident ray will be equal to the critical angle, θ_c.

Example: A transparent plastic has a refractive index of 1·58. What will be the critical angle for the plastic?

Answer:

$$n = \frac{1}{\sin \theta_c}$$

$$1 \cdot 58 = \frac{1}{\sin \theta_c}$$

$$\sin \theta_c = \frac{1}{1 \cdot 58}$$

$$\theta_c = 39 \cdot 3°$$

☑TQ 38 A ray of light strikes the surface of a glass block as shown below. Determine if the ray is totally internally reflected or escapes from the glass at point X.

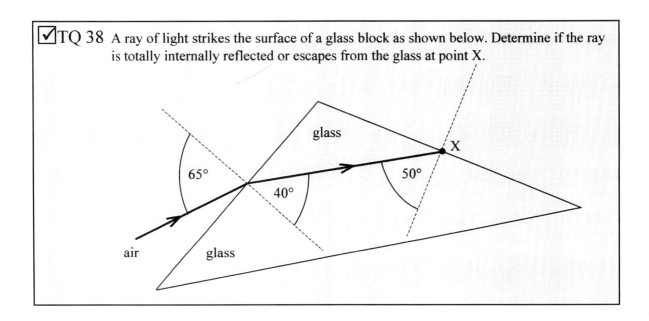

Optoelectronics and Semiconductors

Light Intensity

The intensity of light falling on a surface is defined as the power per unit area i.e. the watts per square metre. Thus

$$\text{intensity} = \frac{\text{power}}{\text{area}} \qquad I = \frac{P}{A}$$

where I = light intensity in watts per square metre (W m⁻²)

P = power in watts (W)

A = area in metres squared (m²)

☑TQ 39 A slide projector projects light onto a screen which measures 2 m by 1·5 m. Find the intensity of the light if the rate at which energy falls on the screen is 300 W.

The Inverse Square Law

As the distance from a light source increases the light intensity decreases. The relationship between light intensity and distance can be found using the apparatus shown below.

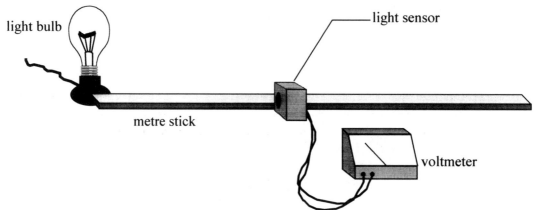

The light sensor produces a voltage which is proportional to the intensity of the light falling on it. This can be measured at a range of distances from the light bulb in an otherwise completely dark room. A graph of light intensity against distance produces the first graph shown.

By plotting a graph of light intensity against the inverse of the distance squared, as shown in the second graph, a straight line through the origin is obtained.

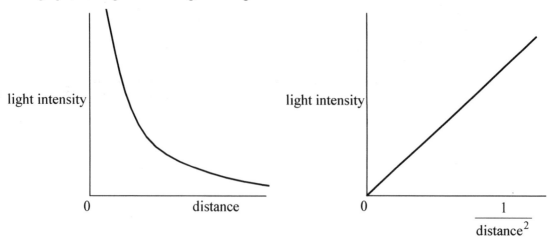

The straight line through the origin proves that light intensity is directly proportional to the inverse of the distance squared:

$$\text{light intensity} \propto \frac{1}{\text{distance}^2} \qquad\qquad I \propto \frac{1}{d^2}$$

A formula can be obtained from this relationship for the change in light intensity with changing distance from a point light source i.e.

$$I_1 d_1^2 = I_2 d_2^2$$

I = light intensity in watts per square metre (W m^{-2})
d = distance in metres (m)

☑TQ 40 The light intensity on a table top from a lamp suspended 0·8 m above it is 10 W m^{-2}. What will the light intensity be if the lamp is raised to a height of 2·0 m?

Photoelectric effect

The photoelectric effect occurs when electromagnetic radiation is directed at a metal surface and ejects electrons from the metal. This is often demonstrated using a zinc plate on a gold leaf electroscope and shining ultra violet light on the plate.

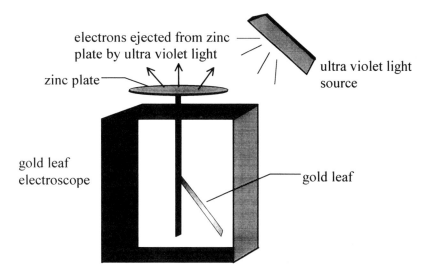

electrons ejected from zinc plate by ultra violet light

zinc plate

ultra violet light source

gold leaf electroscope

gold leaf

The electroscope is given a negative charge which causes the gold leaf to be pushed upwards. When the ultra violet light illuminates the zinc disc at the top of the electroscope the leaf falls. This is due to the electroscope discharging because electrons are ejected from the zinc by the ultra violet light.

This effect cannot be explained by considering light as a continuous wave motion. To deliver enough energy to the zinc the light must be thought of as small bursts of wave energy called **photons**. The energy carried by each photon of light is absorbed by one electron and this allows one electron per photon to escape from the surface of the zinc plate.

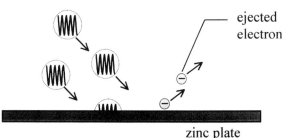

ejected electron

zinc plate

The energy that each photon of light carries can be calculated using the formula:

$$E = hf$$

E = energy in joules (J)
h = Planck's constant in joule seconds (J s)
f = frequency in hertz (Hz)

The formula above shows that the energy a photon of light carries is directly proportional to the frequency of the light and so inversely proportional to the wavelength of the light i.e. the shorter the wavelength the more energy the photon of light will have. All of the photon's energy is absorbed by the electron but it must contain sufficient energy to be able to release the electron.

NOTE:

- When a photon's energy is absorbed by an electron it absorbs all of the photon's energy and not just part of it in order to break free.

- If a white light source is used then the photoelectric effect does not occur as the photons do not have sufficient energy to release electrons. The frequencies of light present in white light are lower than the frequency of ultra violet light.

- The photoelectric effect will not take place if the electroscope is positively charged. This proves that the falling of the gold leaf is not caused by ionisation (as happens when an alpha source is held close to the electroscope) but can only be due to the ejection of electrons since these will not be ejected from a positively charged electroscope (opposite charges attract).

- More electrons are released if a brighter ultra violet light source is used as there will be more photons hitting the metal plate. However, if the light being used does not cause the effect to take place then it will still not occur no matter how bright the light is.

Threshold Frequency and Work Function
The minimum frequency of light required to eject an electron is called the **threshold frequency**, f_0.

The graph opposite shows how there is no photoelectric current below this frequency i.e. no electrons leave the surface of the metal. It also demonstrates that different metals have different threshold frequencies.

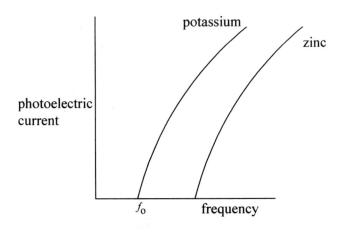

The minimum energy required to release an electron from a metal surface is called the work function and this can be calculated using the formula:

$$\text{work function} = hf_0$$

work function = minimum energy required to release an electron in joules (J)
h = Planck's constant in joule seconds (J s)
f_0 = threshold frequency in hertz (Hz)

☑TQ 41 Light with a frequency of 8.4×10^{14} Hz falls on a metal plate. Show, by calculation, whether the photons of this light will be able to eject electrons if the work function of the metal is 6.0×10^{-19} J.

Kinetic Energy of the Ejected Electron
When the electron is ejected it will have some kinetic energy. The amount of kinetic energy possessed by the electron is equivalent to the excess energy available from the photon after the electron has been ejected:

$$\text{kinetic energy of electron} = \text{energy of photon} - \text{work function}$$

$$E_K = hf - hf_0$$

NOTE:

- If the **frequency** of light being used is increased then the kinetic energy of the ejected electrons increases.

- If the **intensity** of light being used is increased then the number of electrons being ejected increases since there are more photons hitting the metal but the kinetic energy of the ejected electrons remains the same.

Intensity of Radiation and Photons

The photoelectric current (the current leaving the surface at which the photoelectric effect is taking place) is directly proportional to the intensity of the radiation falling on the surface.

A bright light source produces more photons per second than a dim one and this causes more electrons to be ejected as a result. If a number of photons of light, N, are falling on a 1 m^2 surface each second then light intensity can be calculated using;

$$I = Nhf$$

I = intensity in watts per square metre (W m^{-2})
N = number of photons per second per square metre
h = Planck's constant in joule seconds (J s)
f = frequency in hertz (Hz)

☑TQ 42 How many photons per square metre per second are there in a beam of light with an intensity of 8 W m^{-2} if the frequency of the light is 5×10^{14} Hz?

Structure of an Atom

An atom consists of a nucleus (containing protons and neutrons) which is surrounded by orbiting electrons. The electrons are restricted to particular orbits, each orbit having an energy level associated with it. The further from the nucleus the electron's orbit is, the more energy the electron must have to remain in that orbit. The orbits can be thought of as a series of energy levels as shown below.

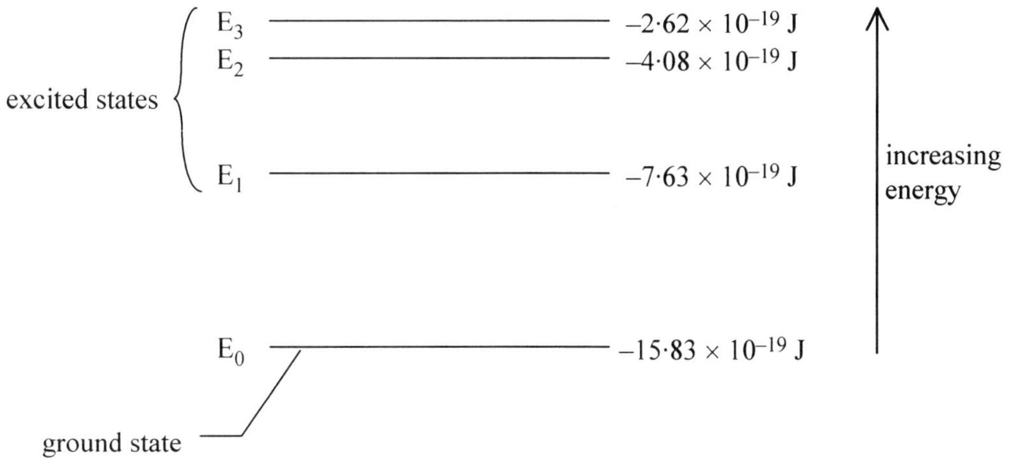

Note:

- The energy level with the least energy is the most negative (E_0) and is called the **ground state**. When an electron gains energy it is said to be in an **excited state** and moves to a higher (less negative) level.

- If the electron gains sufficient energy it can leave the atom altogether and this energy is known as the **ionisation level**.

Emission Line Spectra

The phenomenon of line spectra was met in the Space section of Standard Grade Physics. Line spectra are observed when a light source is observed through a diffraction grating. The light source may be a distant star or an electrical discharge lamp containing vapour of elements such as sodium or mercury.

Bright lines appear corresponding to the frequencies of light present in the light emitted from the lamp. The spectrum shown below is from a sodium discharge lamp.

The bright lines present in a line spectrum are produced by electrons making transitions from an excited state to a less excited state. In the example below there are six different energy jumps which electrons can make from a higher level to a lower level. Each of these transitions would represent a particular line on the line spectra.

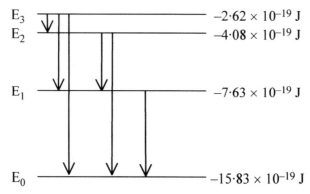

If an electron makes a jump from a high energy level to a lower energy level then energy must be released. The energy released is equivalent to the energy difference between the two levels e.g. an electron dropping from E_2 to E_0 will release $15 \cdot 83 \times 10^{-19} - 4 \cdot 08 \times 10^{-19}$ J $= 11 \cdot 75 \times 10^{-19}$ J. (Although energy levels are negative by convention this can be ignored as far as finding the energy difference between levels is concerned.) The released energy is in the form of light which obeys the formula:

$$W_2 - W_1 = hf$$

W_2 = upper energy level (J)
W_1 = lower energy level (J)
h = Planck's constant in joule seconds (J s)
f = frequency of emitted light in hertz (Hz)

The frequency or wavelength of the emitted light depends upon the amount of energy released when the electron drops down an energy level. Since the electron can only make a jump between discrete energy levels there are only a limited number of frequencies of light emitted. This results in the typical line spectrum observed from different elements. Each element has its own unique set of energy levels and so produces its own set of lines.

NOTE:

- If a spectral line appears brighter than other it is NOT because that frequency is associated with a bigger energy jump than others. It is because there are a higher number of electrons all making the same energy jump so producing more photons of light with the same frequency.

- The photon of light produced by a particular energy jump can be outwith the visible spectrum. If the energy jump is large enough a photon of ultra violet light or X-rays could be obtained.

☑TQ 43 An electron makes a transition from an energy level of $-15\cdot83 \times 10^{-19}$ J to $-3\cdot40 \times 10^{-19}$ J. Calculate the **wavelength** of light produced as a result of this transition.

Absorption Line Spectra

Absorption spectra occur when an electron absorbs the energy of a photon of light in order to increase its energy level. The photon energy must exactly match the energy required by the electron to raise it from one energy level to another.

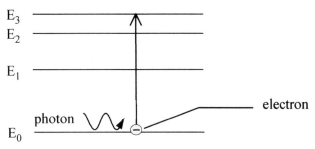

The electron absorbs the photon and so jumps up an energy level. This results in a reduction in the number of photons present with that energy level and of a particular frequency.

The energy level the electron is to rise to can be represented by W_2. This energy level can be calculated using the formula:

$$W_2 = W_1 + hf$$

W_2 = upper energy level (J)
W_1 = lower energy level (J)
hf = energy of absorbed photon (J)

Absorption spectra can be produced by shining white light through the element in a gaseous form. One way of achieving this experimentally is shown below.

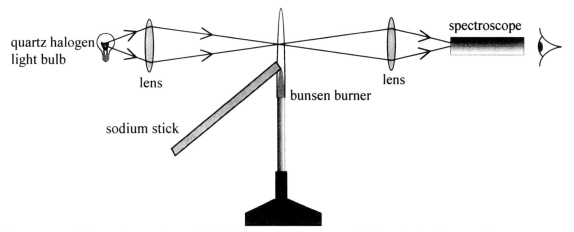

If the source of these photons is a white light source the removal of particular frequencies means the continuous spectrum of that source will have gaps at frequencies where photons have been absorbed. This results in dark bands appearing in the spectrum of the white light. The diagram below shows the absorption spectrum for sodium light. Two dark lines are found where the bright yellow lines of the line emission spectrum are found.

red end of
spectrum

violet end of
spectrum

Absorption lines in Sunlight

If light from the Sun or other stars is passed through a diffraction grating its spectrum is found to have absorption lines present. Gases which are present in the outer part of the Sun absorb photons of particular frequencies and the absorption lines produced as a result correspond to emission lines of particular elements. This allows the elements present in the gas to be identified.

Lasers

An excited electron can fall back naturally to its ground state and in so doing emit a photon of light. This is called **spontaneous emission** and is a random process. The emitted photon of light will travel in a random direction.

In a laser however, **stimulated emission** occurs where an excited electron is encouraged by a photon into making the transition to its ground state.

Laser stands for **L**ight **A**mplification by the **S**timulated **E**mission of **R**adiation. Excited electrons in a laser are stimulated into making the transition to a lower energy level by a photon and emit another photon of light as a result.

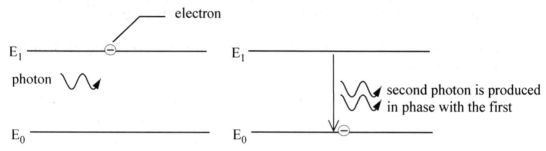

NOTE:

• The energy levels of both photons are the same and so they have the same frequency.

• The direction of travel of each photon is also the same and they will be in phase.

To maintain the laser action the electrons must continually be raised into an excited state. This is achieved by an 'electron pump'. The photons produced by stimulated emission travel through the laser gas and cause more electrons to make the jump from an excited state to the ground state so producing more photons. These strike the mirrors at either end of the laser tube and are reflected back into the gas so creating an ever more intense beam of laser light. One of the mirrors is only partially reflecting and this allows some of the photons to escape as the laser beam.

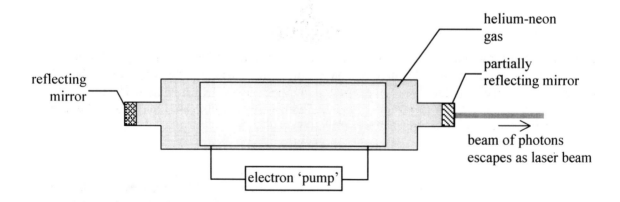

NOTE:

- Laser light is monochromatic i.e. all the photons have the same frequency.

- The laser beam is coherent with all the photons in phase.

- The laser beam does not spread out like light from an ordinary light source. Instead the laser beam retains a small diameter making it a very intense light source. A 0·1 mW beam is powerful enough to cause eye damage.

Insulators, Conductors and Semiconductors
Materials can be divided into three categories of substance according to their electrical properties:

- **conductors**—contain many free electrons and conduct easily e.g. metals, carbon;

- **insulators**—few free electrons and do not conduct e.g. plastic, rubber, glass;

- **semiconductors**—behave as insulators when pure but when an impurity is added to them they can be made to conduct under certain circumstances e.g. silicon and germanium.

Doping
The process of adding an impurity atoms to a pure semiconductor is known as **doping**.

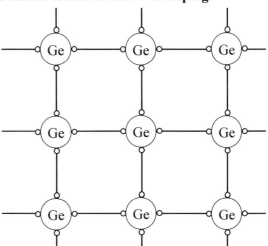

Pure germanium has four outer electrons available for bonding and this will allow it to combine with other germanium atoms and share their outer electrons. This makes for a very stable atom which has no free electrons to conduct.

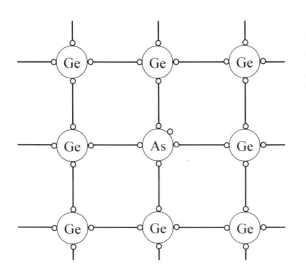

Some of the germanium atoms can be replaced with similar atoms of arsenic. These have five outer electrons and when they combine with the germanium atoms there is one extra electron left free to conduct for each arsenic atom since only four electrons are required to combine with other atoms.

Since there are now unattached electrons (**negative charges**) free to conduct this type of semiconductor is known as **n-type semiconductor**. This material is electrically neutral since all electrons present are balanced by protons present in either germanium or arsenic atoms.

In **p-type semiconductor** material some atoms can be replaced with indium atoms which each have only three outer electrons. This creates a gap into which neighbouring atoms can move. This is known as a **positive hole**.

P-type semiconductor material is electrically neutral since all electrons present are balanced by protons present in either germanium or indium atoms.

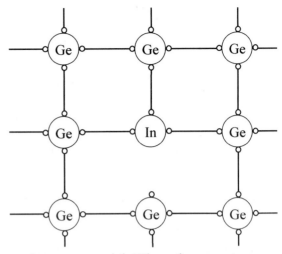

The p-n Junction

It is possible to grow a crystal containing both n-type and p-type material. Where these meet a layer is formed called the **depletion layer**. This is because electrons from the n-type layer have migrated into the p-type material and positive holes from the p-type material have migrated into the n-type material.

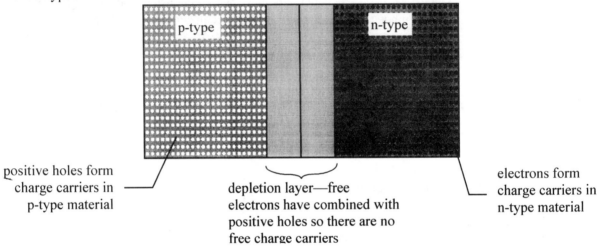

positive holes form charge carriers in p-type material

depletion layer—free electrons have combined with positive holes so there are no free charge carriers

electrons form charge carriers in n-type material

The depletion layer is now devoid of charge carriers as the positive holes and electrons have combined together. The effect of this is to produce a potential difference across the depletion layer which opposes the movement of any further electrons or positive holes across the layer.

Biasing the p-n Junction

The p-n junction described above is better known as a **diode**. By applying a voltage to the junction it is possible to make it behave in a particular manner. This is known as biasing the junction.

If a cell is connected in such a way that the negative of the cell is connected to the p-type material and the positive to the n-type the diode is said to be **reverse biased**. Positive holes will be attracted towards the negative terminal of the cell and free electrons to the positive terminal of the cell. In this way the depletion layer is made larger and the diode will not conduct.

If the cell is reversed then the diode will now conduct. Positive holes flow through into the depletion layer towards the negative terminal of the cell and free electrons flow into the depletion layer towards the positive terminal of the cell. The depletion layer now disappears and the diode conducts. It is said to be **forward biased**.

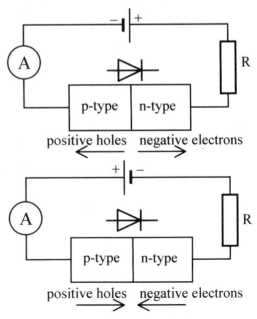

Light Emitting Diode

A light emitting diode contains a p-n junction and behaves in much the same way as an ordinary diode—it must be forward biased in order to conduct. When forward biased the diode will also emit light as a result of positive holes and electrons recombining and releasing energy in the form of photons of light.

The light produced by the LED will obey the equation $E = hf$ where E is the recombination energy of the positive hole and the electron and f is the frequency of light emitted.

The symbol for an LED is shown opposite.

Photodiode

A photodiode is also composed of a p-n junction and has the symbol opposite.

A photodiode has a small transparent case through which light can enter. When light falls on the p-n junction the photons of light provide energy for an electron-positive hole pair to be produced. If the intensity of light on the photodiode is increased then more photons fall on the p-n junction and more electron-positive hole pairs will be released. Photodiodes may be connected in a circuit in a number of ways.

Photovoltaic mode

In this mode the photodiode is popularly known as a solar cell. The diode is used to provide the voltage supply for a device e.g. a calculator. When light falls on the photodiode electron-positive hole pairs are formed and this creates an e.m.f. across the p-n junction. If a large number of photodiodes are connected together then a solar panel is produced.

Photoconductive mode

In this mode the photodiode is used a light sensor. The photodiode is connected in reverse bias so that it does not normally conduct. When light falls on the photodiode however, there will be a number of electron-positive hole pairs produced which can act as charge carriers and so a current can flow (called the reverse leakage current).

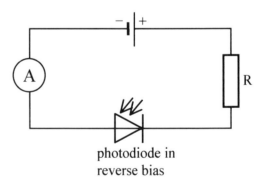

photodiode in reverse bias

The size of current which can flow will depend upon the number of charge carriers produced which in turn depends upon the light intensity falling on the photodiode. The reverse leakage current is directly proportional to the light intensity.

Note:

- The reverse leakage current does not depend upon the reverse-biasing voltage.

- The photodiode is capable of switching on and off very quickly which makes it suitable for use in devices such as optical fibre signal receivers.

MOSFET Transistors

MOSFET stands for **M**etal **O**xide **S**emiconductor **F**ield **E**ffect **T**ransistor (there's no need to learn this!). They are a very common type of transistor used by industry and carry out the same function as the transistors studied at Standard Grade.

The MOSFET transistor examined here is the n-channel enhancement type. There are three connections to a MOSFET transistor and the symbol for this transistor is shown below.

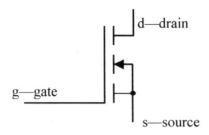

The connections to the MOSFET transistor are called the gate, source and drain.

How the MOSFET Works

The MOSFET transistor consists of a block of p-type semiconductor in which two implants are made of n-type semiconductor. The connections to the source, gate, drain and substrate are made by metal contacts. A cross-section through an n-channel enhancement type MOSFET device is shown below.

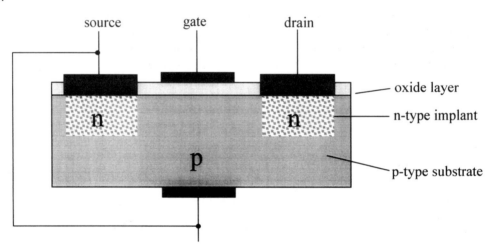

When a positive voltage is applied to the gate free electrons in the p-type substrate are attracted up to form the conducting channel just below the gate

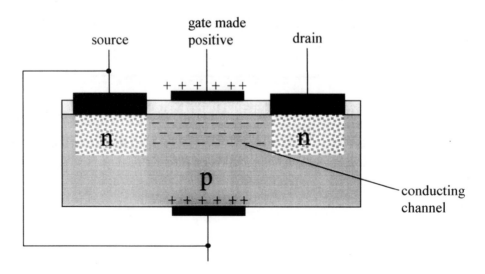

When a voltage is applied between the drain and the source, as shown in the diagram below, a current flows from the source through the conducting channel to the drain.

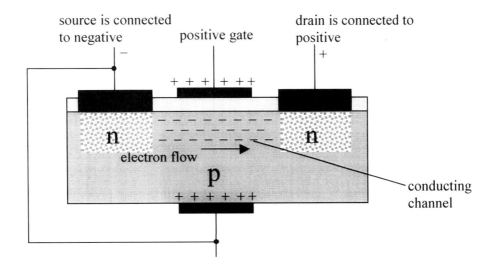

By applying a positive voltage to the gate the MOSFET transistor is switched ON. Applying a zero or negative voltage to the gate will switch the MOSFET OFF. The example shown below is used to switch on a lamp.

If V_1 is made positive (above 1·8 V) the transistor is switched ON and the lamp will light.

The MOSFET transistor can also be used as an amplifier. Varying the voltage applied to the gate will vary the current flowing between the source and the drain.

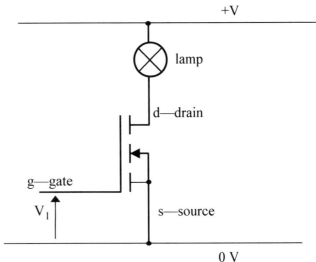

Nuclear Reactions

Rutherford's Alpha Particle Scattering Experiment

At the start of this century scientists thought of an atom as being made up of a ball of positive charge in which was embedded the negatively charged electrons. This was known as the 'plum pudding model' and it fitted the experimental evidence available at the time.

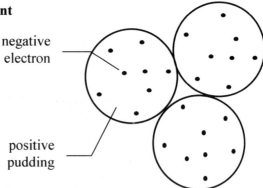

A new experiment was proposed by Ernest Rutherford and carried out by two researchers called Geiger and Marsden, in which alpha particles were fired at a piece of very thin gold foil.
A fluorescent screen was placed around the experiment and alpha particles striking this caused it to emit tiny flashes of light. The flashes of light were observed through a microscope and could be counted at various positions around the foil. The whole apparatus was enclosed in a vacuum as otherwise the air molecules present would deflect the path of the alpha particles.

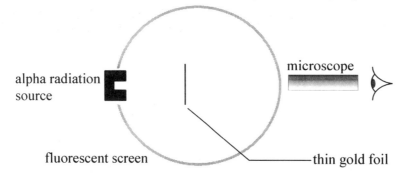

It was discovered that most flashes occurred opposite the foil as the alpha particles passed straight through it. A significant number, however, were scattered at an angle and some even bounced back in the direction they had come. The plum pudding model could not be used to explain these observations so a new model of the atom was devised. In this model:

* the nucleus has a relatively small diameter compared to that of the atom—most alpha particles passed straight through;

* most of the mass is concentrated in the nucleus—alpha particles hitting nucleus bounced back;

* the nucleus has a positive charge—the positively charged alpha particles are repelled or deflected.

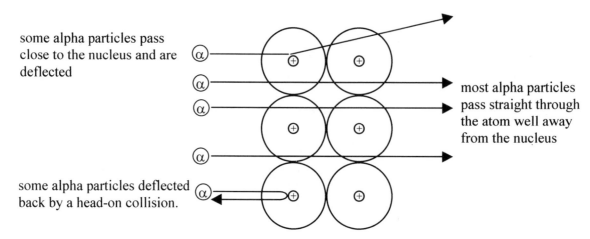

The model given above is the model of an atom we still use today.

Summary of Radiation Properties

The table below summarises the properties of the three types of ionising radiation studied at Standard Grade.

Name of radiation	Symbol	What is it?	Stopped by	Amount of ionisation it produces
alpha	α	2 protons and 2 neutrons	thin sheet of paper or a few cm of air	strongly ionises
beta	β	a fast-moving electron	about 3 mm of aluminium	weakly ionises
gamma	γ	a wave and part of the electromagnetic spectrum	about 3 cm of lead	weakly ionises

Radioactive decay

Atoms are classified according to the number of protons (positively charged) in the nucleus. Also in the nucleus are found neutrons (neutral charge) and orbiting around the nucleus are electrons (negatively charged). The number of electrons will normally be the same as the number of protons so making the atom neutral in charge. The symbol for an atom is often written in the form shown below.

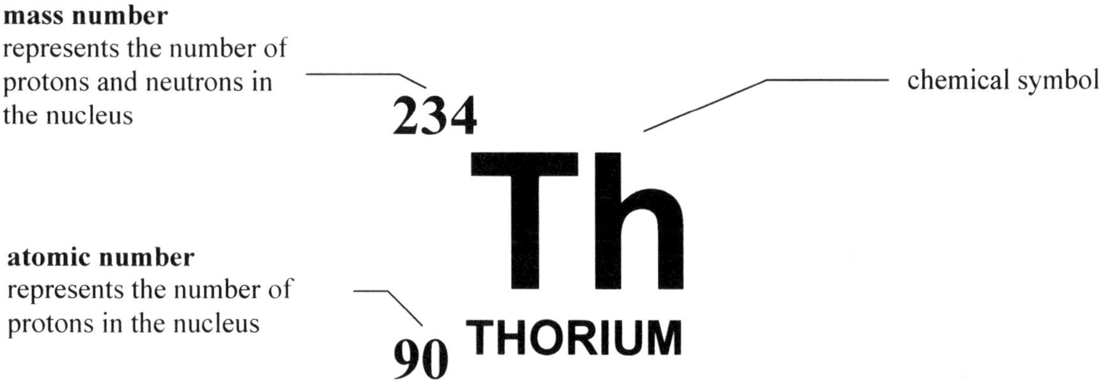

mass number
represents the number of protons and neutrons in the nucleus

234

chemical symbol

Th

atomic number
represents the number of protons in the nucleus

90 THORIUM

The number of protons in the nucleus is given by the atomic number. Subtracting the atomic number from the mass number will give the number of neutrons in the nucleus.

Nuclei of the same element will all have the same number of protons. Elements which have different numbers of neutrons present the nucleus are called isotopes e.g. $^{238}_{92}U$ and $^{235}_{92}U$.

Atoms of heavy elements with large numbers of protons and neutrons tend to be unstable and undergo a process of radioactive decay into lighter elements.

Alpha decay

Alpha decay occurs when a particle consisting of 2 protons and 2 neutrons (a helium nucleus) is ejected from an atom's nucleus. An alpha particle is represented in equations by $^{4}_{2}He$.

When an alpha particle is ejected from the atom of a nucleus the atomic number will decrease by 2 and the mass number will decrease by 4 to give the nucleus of a new element e.g.

$$^{238}_{92}U \rightarrow ^{234}_{90}Th + ^{4}_{2}He$$

Note that the total atomic number and the total mass number on each side of the equation is the same i.e. $90 + 2 = 92$ and $234 + 4 = 238$.

Beta Decay

Beta decay occurs when a particle consisting of a fast moving electron is ejected from an atom's nucleus. A beta particle is represented in equations by $_{-1}^{0}e$.

The beta particle is produced by the break up of a neutron into a proton and electron with the electron being ejected as the beta particle and the proton remaining behind in the nucleus.

When this occurs the atomic number will increase by 1 due to the presence of the additional proton and the mass number will remain unchanged as the total number of particles in the nucleus is unchanged (neutron lost and a proton gained).
e.g.

$$_{91}^{234}Pa \rightarrow {}_{92}^{234}U + {}_{-1}^{0}e$$

Note that the total atomic number and the total mass number on each side of the equation is the same i.e. $92 + -1 = 91$ and $234 + 0 = 234$.

Gamma Decay

Gamma radiation does not involve the ejection of a particle from the nucleus of an atom. Instead the gamma ray is an electromagnetic wave which is produced from an excited nucleus. The loss of energy due to the emission of the gamma radiation brings the nucleus into a more stable state.

Equations of Decay

It is possible to determine the products produced by a series of decays by looking at the atomic and mass numbers of the isotopes at the beginning and end of the decay series. To solve these problems it is important to remember that:

- for alpha decay the **atomic number decreases** by two and the **mass number decreases** by four;

- for beta decay the **atomic number increases** by one and the **mass number remains unchanged**;

- for a chain of several decays there may be a combination of these occurring.
  (The secret is seeing what combination of decays will fit the atomic and mass numbers!)

Consider the decay chain shown below:

$$_{84}^{218}Po \rightarrow {}_{82}^{214}Pb \rightarrow {}_{83}^{214}Bi \rightarrow {}_{84}^{214}Po$$

The decay from $_{84}^{218}Po$ to $_{82}^{214}Pb$ resulted in the emission of an alpha particle. The decay of $_{82}^{214}Pb$ to $_{83}^{214}Bi$ and then to $_{84}^{214}Po$ resulted in the emission of two beta particles. Since the isotope produced as a result of these decays now has 84 protons we are back to the original element i.e. Polonium (Po).

☑TQ 44   Find the number of alpha and beta particles produced when $_{91}^{234}Pa$ decays to $_{88}^{226}Ra$.

Nuclear Fission

Nuclear fission occurs when a large heavy nucleus splits up into two smaller nuclei and in so doing releases neutrons ($_0^1 n$) and energy. The fission process may occur spontaneously of its own accord but can be induced to happen by bombarding a large nucleus with neutrons. This causes the nucleus to become unstable and undergo fission to achieve stability.

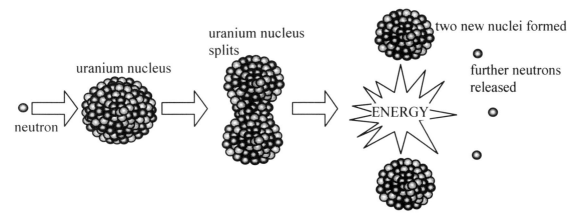

uranium nucleus

uranium nucleus splits

two new nuclei formed

further neutrons released

neutron

ENERGY

Examples of this type of reaction are shown below.

$$_{100}^{256} Fm \rightarrow {}_{54}^{140} Xe + {}_{46}^{112} Pd + 4\ {}_0^1 n + energy \qquad \textbf{spontaneous fission}$$

$$_0^1 n + {}_{92}^{235} U \rightarrow {}_{56}^{141} Ba + {}_{36}^{92} Kr + 3\ {}_0^1 n + energy \qquad \textbf{induced fission}$$

Induced fission is used in devices such as the reactors in nuclear power stations. Neutrons bombard uranium nuclei and these produce energy when they split. The additional neutrons produced remain within the reactor and go on to produce further fissions.

In both the equations given above the mass of the products is less than the mass of the starting materials. The energy produced through nuclear fission is due to mass being converted into energy. Energy and mass are jointly conserved i.e. mass can be converted into energy and energy can be converted into mass.

Albert Einstein produced an equation to relate the change between mass and energy:

$$E\ =\ m\ c^2 \qquad \text{where } E\ =\ \text{energy in joules (J)}$$
$$m\ =\ \text{change in mass in kilograms (kg)}$$
$$c\ =\ \text{speed of light in metres per second (m s}^{-1})$$

Nuclear Fusion

Nuclear fusion is the reaction which takes place in the Sun. In this reaction two small nuclei come together and join to form a larger nucleus. The reaction for a typical fusion reaction is shown below.

$$_1^2 H + {}_1^2 H \rightarrow {}_2^3 He + {}_0^1 n + energy$$

In the instance shown above two nuclei from an isotope of hydrogen have joined together to form a nucleus of an isotope of helium plus a neutron. The mass of the products is less than the mass of the starting materials as mass is again changed into energy.

As in nuclear fission, the difference in mass between the left hand side and right hand side of the equation is used to calculate the energy released by the reaction.

Calculating the Energy Released by Fission and Fusion

The energy released by a reaction can be calculated by finding the difference in mass between each side of the equation. The calculation shown below is for a fission reaction but the same technique is applied to a fusion reaction.

Example: Find the energy released as a result of the following nuclear reaction.

$$^{235}_{92}U + ^{1}_{0}n \rightarrow ^{140}_{58}Ce + ^{94}_{40}Zr + ^{1}_{0}n + ^{1}_{0}n + energy$$

mass of $^{235}_{92}U$ $= 390 \cdot 173 \times 10^{-27}$ kg

mass of $^{140}_{58}Ce$ $= 232 \cdot 242 \times 10^{-27}$ kg

mass of $^{94}_{40}Zr$ $= 155 \cdot 883 \times 10^{-27}$ kg

mass of $^{1}_{0}n$ $= 1 \cdot 675 \times 10^{-27}$ kg

Total mass on Left Hand Side	Total mass on Right Hand Side
$^{235}_{92}U$ $390 \cdot 173 \times 10^{-27}$	$^{140}_{58}Ce$ $232 \cdot 242 \times 10^{-27}$
$^{1}_{0}n$ $\underline{1 \cdot 675 \times 10^{-27}}$	$^{94}_{40}Zr$ $155 \cdot 883 \times 10^{-27}$
$391 \cdot 848 \times 10^{-27}$ kg	$^{1}_{0}n$ $1 \cdot 675 \times 10^{-27}$
	$^{1}_{0}n$ $\underline{1 \cdot 675 \times 10^{-27}}$
	$391 \cdot 475 \times 10^{-27}$ kg

$$\text{change in mass} = 391 \cdot 848 \times 10^{-27} - 391 \cdot 475 \times 10^{-27}$$
$$= 3 \cdot 73 \times 10^{-28} \text{ kg}$$

Calculate the energy released by using the change in mass in the equation $E = m c^2$

$E = m c^2$

$E = 3 \cdot 73 \times 10^{-28} \times (3 \times 10^8)^2$

$E = 3 \cdot 36 \times 10^{-11}$ J

☑TQ 45   In the nuclear reaction shown below, two nuclei of deuterium, an isotope of hydrogen, combine together to form an isotope of helium.

$$^{2}_{1}D + ^{2}_{1}D \rightarrow ^{3}_{2}He + ^{1}_{0}n + energy$$

(a)   What name is given to this type of reaction?

(b)   Use the data given below to calculate the energy released as a result of the reaction.

mass of $^{2}_{1}D$ $= 3 \cdot 342 \times 10^{-27}$ kg

mass of $^{3}_{2}He$ $= 5 \cdot 005 \times 10^{-27}$ kg

mass of $^{1}_{0}n$ $= 1 \cdot 675 \times 10^{-27}$ kg

Dosimetry and safety

Activity of a Source

A radioactive substance will contain many nuclei which undergo decay in a random manner. The rate of this decay is known as the **activity** of the substance and is given by the formula:

$$\text{activity} = \frac{\text{number of nuclei decaying}}{\text{time in seconds}} \qquad A = \frac{N}{t}$$

where A = activity in becquerels (Bq)
N = number of nuclei decaying
t = time in seconds (s)

Activity is measured in becquerels and 1 Bq is equivalent to 1 decay per second.

☑TQ 46 A radioactive substance has an activity of 2 MBq. How many decays will occur in a time of 1 minute?

Absorbed Dose

When alpha, beta or gamma radiation is absorbed by the human body its energy is deposited in the absorbing tissue. This is measured by the absorbed dose which is the energy absorbed per unit mass of the absorbing material.

$$\text{absorbed dose} = \frac{\text{energy}}{\text{mass}} \qquad D = \frac{E}{m}$$

where D = absorbed dose in grays (Gy)
E = energy in joules (J)
m = mass in kilograms (kg)

One gray is equivalent to one joule of energy being absorbed per kilogram of body tissue.

Dose Equivalent

The harm done to human tissue will depend upon a number of factors.

* The size of the absorbed dose.

* The type of radiation being absorbed, whether it is alpha, beta, gamma neutrons or X-rays.

Since the absorbed dose, D, is only measuring the energy deposited in the tissue and does not take these other factors into account, it is necessary to have another unit called the **sievert**. The sievert is a unit which applies a quality factor, Q, to the absorbed dose so that the type of radiation can be taken into account.

$$\text{dose equivalent} = \text{absorbed dose} \times \text{quality factor}$$

$$H = D\,Q$$

where H = dose equivalent in sieverts (Sv)
D = absorbed dose in grays (Gy)
Q = quality factor

Example quality factors are shown below. These do not have to be learned but it can be noted that alpha particles have a high quality factor due to their strong ionising effect which causes a lot of damage to cells.

Type of radiation	Quality factor, Q
X-rays	1
gamma rays	1
beta particles	1
slow neutrons	5
fast neutrons	10
alpha particles	20

Dose Equivalent Rate

People who work with radiation over long periods of time must have their exposure to radiation carefully controlled. The dose equivalent rate, $\dot{H}$, (H dot) is used to indicate the rate at which radiation is being absorbed.

$$\text{dose equivalent rate} = \frac{\text{dose equivalent}}{\text{time}} \qquad \dot{H} = \frac{H}{t}$$

where $\dot{H}$ = dose equivalent rate in sieverts per hour, year (Sv h^{-1}, Sv yr^{-1})
H = dose equivalent in sieverts (Sv)
t = time in seconds, hours or years

☑TQ 47   A welder uses radioactive substances to check the quality of the welds joining pipes together. In the course of the tests he receives a total of 20 µGy of gamma radiation over a period of 40 hours.

(a)   What dose equivalent would be logged for his exposure during the tests?

(b)   What is the dose equivalent rate he received?

Effective Dose Equivalent

Another measurement can be made called the effective dose equivalent which takes into account the body tissue or organ being exposed. Some types of cells are more susceptible to damage than others e.g. cells in the reproductive system.

Background Radiation

Members of the general public will receive a dosage of radiation from background radiation, both natural and man-made. The relative proportions of this radiation is shown in the graph below.

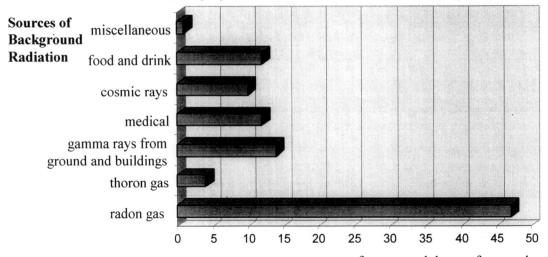

Sources of Background Radiation

percentage of our annual dosage from each source

NOTE:
- Miscellaneous sources include nuclear discharges, radiation received at work, nuclear fallout from atomic tests and other sources.

- Cosmic rays are from outer space and the atmosphere absorbs most of this radiation. Your dosage will increase if you fly in high-flying planes.

- Radiation from medical sources will vary a lot from individual to individual depending on whether you require any X-rays or treatment involving radiation.

- Radon and Thoron gases make up most of the dosage we receive from background radiation. These gases come from rocks underground and the amount present depends on the geology of the area in which you live.

The dosage that we receive from natural sources totals approximately **2 mSv** per year. The maximum amount of radiation that members of the general public should receive is set as an **annual effective dose equivalent**. People who work with radiation will often have a higher limit set for them than members of the public. The total dosage that these workers receive is carefully monitored and controlled (e.g by using radiation badges).

Radiation and Absorber Thickness

If a thickness of material is placed in front of a radioactive source it will absorb some of the radiation. An experiment can be carried out to investigate this effect and the apparatus for this is shown below.

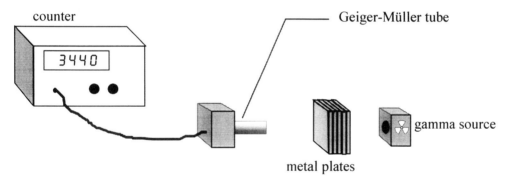

A Geiger-Müller tube is placed in a laboratory and the background count measured. A gamma source is then placed a fixed distance from the G-M tube. Plates of the material under investigation can then be placed between the source and the G-M tube and the count rate measured at various thicknesses of material. The background count would be deducted from the values obtained to give the true count rate penetrating the material. The shape of the graph will be familiar as it is exactly the same as that obtained when the half-life of a radioactive substance is measured.

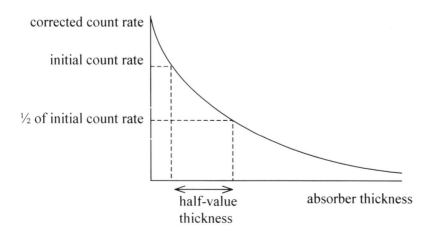

It is possible to find the **half-value thickness** from the graph i.e. the thickness of material required to reduce the count rate by one half. This value will be the same no matter what part of the graph it is measured from.

The effectiveness of an absorber is often described by quoting its half thickness—the lower the half-value thickness the better the material is at absorbing radiation.

Radiation and Distance

Gamma radiation is an electromagnetic wave and so, like light, will obey the inverse square law:

$$\text{intensity of radiation} \propto \frac{1}{\text{distance}^2} \qquad I \propto \frac{1}{d^2}$$

For gamma radiation this means that:

$$A \propto \frac{1}{d^2} \qquad \text{or} \qquad H \propto \frac{1}{d^2} \qquad \text{or} \qquad \dot{H} \propto \frac{1}{d^2}$$

An effective method or reducing the radiation dose received is to increase the distance from the source.

☑TQ 48 A composite material has a half-value thickness of 1·2 cm.

(a)   What thickness would a wall of this material have to be to reduce the activity from a source from 4000 μSv to 125 μSv?

(b)   Explain why people handling sources use long-handled tongs and hold the source well away from their body.

Units, Prefixes and Scientific Notation

Using the correct units

When answering questions ensure that the correct SI unit is used after every numerical answer e.g. velocity is measured in m s^{-1} and acceleration in m s^{-2} etc.

All the ones that you will use in this course are given in the table below.

Quantity	*SI Unit*	*Abbreviation*
Velocity	metres per second	m s^{-1}
Speed	metres per second	m s^{-1}
Distance	metres	m
Displacement	metres	m
Time	seconds	s
Acceleration	metres per second per second	m s^{-2}
Force	newtons	N
Momentum	kilograms metres per second	kg m s^{-1}
Impulse	newton seconds, kilograms metres per second	N s, kg m s^{-1}
Mass	kilograms	kg
Pressure	pascals, newtons per square metre	Pa, N m^{-2}
Area	square metres	m^{-2}
Volume	cubic metres	m^{-3}
Temperature	kelvin, degrees celsius	K, °C
Density	kilograms per cubic metre	kg m^{-3}
Work, Energy	joules	J
Power	watts, joules per second	W, J s^{-1}
Charge	coulombs	C
Voltage or potential difference	volts	V
Current	amperes	A
Resistance	ohms	Ω
Capacitance	farads	F
Frequency	hertz	Hz
Period	seconds	s
Wavelength	metres	m
Intensity	watts per square metre	W m^{-2}
Activity	becquerels	Bq
Absorbed dose	grays	Gy
Absorbed dose equivalent	sieverts	Sv
Absorbed dose equivalent rate	sieverts per hour	Sv h^{-1}

Scientific notation

If using very large or very small numbers they can be quoted using scientific notation or standard index form e.g. the speed of light as 3×10^8 m/s,

Here is a large number in ordinary form:

$$6\ 800\ 000 \cdot 0$$

This can be converted to scientific notation by moving the decimal point to give a number between 1 and 10 i.e. $6 \cdot 8 \times 10^6$. The decimal point was moved six times to the left hence $\times\ \mathbf{10^6}$.

Small numbers are treated in a similar way e.g. $0 \cdot 000\ 35$ becomes $3 \cdot 5 \times 10^{-4}$ since the decimal point was moved 4 places to the right.

Entering scientific notation into a calculator

Calculators will have either an [EXP] or [EE] key on your calculator. These keys are used to enter the number into a calculator as shown below.

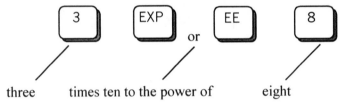

three   times ten to the power of   eight

which will then be displayed

Prefixes to units

Units will often have a prefix e.g. 1 kΩ means one thousand ohms. The prefixes used in this course are shown in the table below.

Prefix	Symbol	Factor	
giga	G	1 000 000 000	$= 1 \times 10^9$
mega	M	1 000 000	$= 1 \times 10^6$
kilo	k	1000	$= 1 \times 10^3$
milli	m	$0 \cdot 001$	$= 1 \times 10^{-3}$
micro	μ	$0 \cdot 000\ 001$	$= 1 \times 10^{-6}$
nano	n	$0 \cdot 000\ 000\ 001$	$= 1 \times 10^{-9}$
pico	p	$0 \cdot 000\ 000\ 0001$	$= 1 \times 10^{-12}$

Significant figures

A number of questions in the Higher course involving performing calculations. It is important that the answers to an appropriate number of significant figures. As a general rule, quote the answer you give to the same number of significant figures as the values provided in the question.

Uncertainties

Types of Uncertainty

Whenever a measurement is made in an experiment it will be subject to an uncertainty.
There are three types of uncertainty which can be identified:

- *Random uncertainties* When repeated measurements are made of the same quantity there is likely to be a spread of results obtained e.g. if five people were to time the swing of a pendulum they would all obtain slightly different results.

- *Reading uncertainties* A measuring instrument such as a meter stick can only be read with a certain degree of accuracy depending on the scale markings on it. The reading uncertainty is determined by the accuracy to which we can read the scale.

- *Systematic uncertainties* These occur when there is a mistake in the way an experiment is carried out or an instrument is wrongly calibrated e.g. a voltmeter might not be set to its zero value properly.

All of these can produce a value which is above or below the true value.

Finding the Mean Value

When taking readings from an experiment it is always a good idea to take repeated measurements and calculate the mean value from these. By making repeated measurements the random uncertainty is reduced. The best estimate of the true value is given by the **mean value**. The mean value is found by adding together all the readings and then dividing by the number of readings taken.

$$\text{mean value} = \frac{\text{sum of all measurements}}{\text{number of measurements made}}$$

If there has been a systematic uncertainty present then the mean value will differ from the true value e.g. if a voltmeter is not set at zero and is always reading 0·5 V too high, the mean voltage will be 0·5 V too high.

Approximate Random Uncertainty in the Mean

Once the mean value has been found the approximate random uncertainty in the mean can be calculated. This is found used using the formula:

$$\text{approximate random uncertainty in mean} = \frac{\text{maximum value} - \text{minimum value}}{\text{number of readings taken}}$$

☑TQ 49 An experiment is carried out in which a temperature is measured. Five readings are taken for this temperature and these are shown below.

$$80·8°C, \quad 81·0°C, \quad 80·3°C, \quad 80·9°C, \quad 81·2°C$$

(*a*) Find the mean value of the readings.

(*b*) Calculate the approximate random uncertainty in the mean.

Estimating the Uncertainty When Using Meters

Whenever the scale on a meter is read there is a certain amount of judgement made about what the exact reading is.

Analogue meters: For analogue meters the uncertainty is taken as being one half of the smallest division on the scale e.g. a meter stick marked off in millimetres will have a reading uncertainty of 0·5 mm.

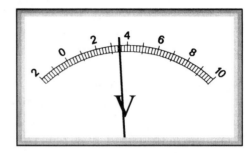

The voltmeter shown opposite has a scale which is marked of in 0·2 V divisions so the accuracy with which it can be read is to 0·1 V, usually written as ±0·1 V.

Digital meters: A digital meter may appear to give a very accurate answer but the number displayed may not be the actual value being measured. The true value may be slightly above or below it but not enough for the meter to display the next value. When using a digital meter the uncertainty is taken as being equivalent to the smallest scale reading.

The digital voltmeter shown opposite has a scale in which the smallest division is 0·1 mV. This is taken as the uncertainty in the reading i.e. ±0·1 mV.

Expressing uncertainties

Uncertainties can be expressed in **absolute form** such as ±0·1 V, ±0·05 mm etc. It is also possible to express uncertainties in **percentage form**. In percentage form the uncertainty is expressed as a percentage of the total reading. This is more meaningful and indicates how 'serious' the uncertainty is in terms of the measurement being made.

$$\text{percentage uncertainty} = \frac{\text{absolute uncertainty}}{\text{measurement to which uncertainty is applied}} \times \frac{100}{1}$$

Suppose a thermometer gives a reading of 58°C with an uncertainty of 0·5°C.

This uncertainty can be quoted as either an absolute uncertainty: 58°C ±0·5°C

or

as a percentage uncertainty: 58°C ±0·86% $\left(\dfrac{0\cdot5}{58} \times \dfrac{100}{1} = 0\cdot86\% \right)$

Using Percentage Uncertainties

Percentage uncertainties are also useful where several different measurements are made in the course of an experiment. For example suppose the following results were obtained during an experiment to find the resistance of a resistor using Ohm's Law.

voltage $= 6.8$ V ± 0.2 V.   percentage uncertainty $= 2.9\%$
current $= 1.4$ A ± 0.1 A   percentage uncertainty $= 7.1\%$

The greatest uncertainty is in the measurement of current and this is the uncertainty applied to the final answer.

By calculation $\quad V = IR$
$$6.8 = 1.4 \times R$$
$$R = \frac{6.8}{1.4}$$
$$R = 4.9 \ \Omega$$

The largest percentage uncertainty is applied to the answer to give $R = 4.9 \ \Omega \pm 7.1\%$

This can be converted back into an absolute uncertainty by finding 7.1% of the final answer. This gives $R = 4.9 \pm 0.4 \ \Omega$.

☑TQ 50 During experiments on motion it is necessary to measure the speed of a vehicle on a linear air track. This is achieved by using light gates and measuring the length of the vehicle. The results obtained are as follows:

length of vehicle $= 150 \pm 0.5$ mm
time light gate beam is broken $= 0.2 \pm 0.01$ s

(a) Find the percentage uncertainty in each of the readings.

(b) Calculate the speed of the vehicle quoting the final answer along with the absolute uncertainty.

Appendix (i)—Higher Formulae

UNIT 1 Mechanics and Properties of Matter
Equations of Motion

$$\bar{v} = \frac{s}{t} \quad \text{and} \quad \bar{v} = \frac{u + v}{2}$$

Average speed, u and v in m s^{-1}.

For uniformly accelerated motion,
$$v = u + at$$

$$v^2 = u^2 + 2as$$

v and u in m s^{-1}, a in m s^{-2}, s in m and t in s.

$$s = ut + \tfrac{1}{2}at^2$$

For a velocity v at an angle θ to the horizontal,
$$v_h = v \cos \theta \quad \text{and} \quad v_v = v \sin \theta$$

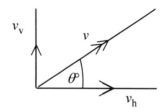

Newton's Second Law

$$F_{un} = ma$$

Force in N, mass in kg and acceleration in m s^{-2}

For an object of weight W on a slope inclined at angle θ to the horizontal,
$$F_{perpendicular} = W \cos \theta$$
$$F_{parallel} = W \sin \theta$$

Force in N.

Momentum and Impulse

$$momentum = m \times v$$

Momentum is in kg m s^{-1}, mass in kg and velocity in m s^{-1}.

$$impulse = \bar{F} \times t$$

Impulse in N s, average force in N and time in s.

$$impulse = \Delta(mv)$$

The unit for impulse can also be kg m s^{-1}.

Density and Pressure

$$\rho = \frac{m}{V}$$

Density is in kg m^{-3}, mass in kg and volume in m^3.

For pressure in a liquid, pressure $\propto$ density $(p \propto \rho)$ and pressure $\propto$ depth $(p \propto h)$
so $p = \rho g h$

The Gas Laws

$$p = \frac{F}{A}$$

Pressure is in Pa, force in N and area in m^2.

$$p_1 V_1 = p_2 V_2$$

for a fixed mass of gas at constant temperature.

$$\frac{p_1}{T_1} = \frac{p_2}{T_2}$$

for a fixed mass of gas at constant volume and where temperature is in kelvin.

$$\frac{V_1}{T_1} = \frac{V_2}{T_2}$$

for a fixed mass of gas at constant pressure and where temperature is in kelvin.

$$\frac{p_1 V_1}{T_1} = \frac{p_2 V_2}{T_2}$$

for a fixed mass of gas where temperature is in kelvin.

UNIT 2 Electricity and Electronics

Electric Fields and Resistors in Circuits

$W = Q V$ Work done (energy) in J, charge in C and voltage in V.

Resistors in a series circuit,

$R_{total} = R_1 + R_2 + R_3$ All resistance values in Ω or all in kΩ.

Resistance in a parallel circuit,

$$\frac{1}{R_{total}} = \frac{1}{R_1} + \frac{1}{R_2} + \frac{1}{R_3}$$ All resistance values in Ω or all in kΩ.

For a circuit with internal resistance,

$E = Ir + IR$ Current in A, resistance in Ω and E in V.

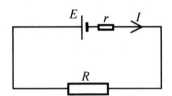

For a balanced Wheatstone bridge,

$$\frac{P}{Q} = \frac{R}{S}$$

For an out of balance Wheatstone bridge.

$\Delta R \propto V$

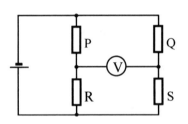

Alternating Current and Voltage

$V_{peak} = V_{rms} \times \sqrt{2}$ $\sqrt{2} \cong 1\cdot4$

$$V_{rms} = \frac{V_{peak}}{\sqrt{2}}$$

The above formulae also apply to current.

Capacitance

$$C = \frac{Q}{V}$$ Capacitance in farads, charge in coulombs and voltage in volts.

$$E = \tfrac{1}{2} Q V = \tfrac{1}{2} C V^2 = \tfrac{1}{2} \frac{Q^2}{C}$$ Energy in joules, capacitance in farads, charge in coulombs and voltage in volts.

$I \propto f$ for a capacitor Current is independent of frequency for a resistor.

Analogue Electronics

Inverting Mode

$$\text{gain} = \frac{V_{\text{out}}}{V_1} = -\frac{R_f}{R_1}$$

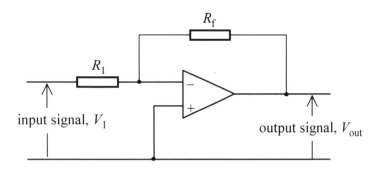

input signal, V_1

output signal, V_{out}

Differential Mode

$$V_{\text{out}} = (V_2 - V_1)\frac{R_f}{R_1}$$

provided $\quad \dfrac{R_f}{R_1} = \dfrac{R_3}{R_2}$

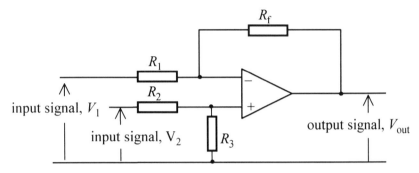

input signal, V_1

input signal, V_2

output signal, V_{out}

UNIT 3 Radiation and Matter
Waves

$$f = \frac{1}{T}$$

Frequency in Hz and time period in s.

For constructive interference
path difference $= n\,\lambda$

where $n = 0, 1, 2, 3, 4, 5, 6$ etc.

For destructive interference
path difference $= (n + \tfrac{1}{2})\,\lambda$

where $n = 0, 1, 2, 3, 4, 5, 6$ etc.

For the nth order fringe of a diffraction grating,
$n\,\lambda = d\sin\theta$

Wavelength and spacing in m.

Refraction of Light
When refraction occurs, the refractive index n is given by,

$$n = \frac{\sin\theta_1}{\sin\theta_2} = \frac{v_1}{v_2} = \frac{\lambda_1}{\lambda_2}$$

When total internal reflection occurs, the critical angle C is given by,

$$\sin C = \frac{1}{n}$$

Optoelectronics and Semiconductors

$$I = \frac{P}{A}$$

Intensity in W m^{-2}, power in W and area in m^2.

$$I \propto \frac{1}{d^2}$$
(i.e. $I_1 d_1^2 = I_2 d_2^2$)

Intensity in W m^{-2} and d in m^2.

$$E = hf$$

Energy in J, h is Planck's constant $= 6\cdot63 \times 10^{-34}$ J s, and frequency in hertz.

$$I = N h f$$

Intensity in W m^{-2}, N is number of photons per second per unit area and f in Hz.

Work Function $= h f_o$

h is Planck's constant and f_o is the threshold frequency in Hz.

$$E_k = hf - h f_o$$

Kinetic energy in J, and f_o and f in Hz.

$$E = W_2 - W_1 = h f$$

Energy in J, W_1 and W_2 energy levels of electron in J, and frequency in Hz.

Nuclear Reactions

$$^{\text{mass number } A}_{\text{atomic number } Z} Q$$

A is number of neutrons + protons, Z is number of protons and Q is the chemical name.

Dosimetry and Safety

$$A = \frac{N}{t}$$

A is activity in becquerels (Bq).

$$D = \frac{E}{m}$$

D is the absorbed dose in grays (Gy).

$$H = D Q$$

H is the absorbed dose equivalent in sieverts (Sv).

$$\dot{H} = \frac{H}{t}$$

$\dot{H}$ is the absorbed dose equivalent rate in sieverts per hour (Sv h^{-1}).

$$E = m c^2$$

Where m is the mass defect and c is 3 x 10^8 m s^{-1}.

FORMULAE TO REMEMBER FROM STANDARD GRADE

wave speed = frequency × wavelength $v = f \lambda$

speed $= \dfrac{\text{distance}}{\text{time}}$ $v = \dfrac{d}{t}$

acceleration $= \dfrac{\text{change in speed}}{\text{time taken for change}}$

acceleration $= \dfrac{\text{final speed - initial speed}}{\text{time taken for change}}$ $a = \dfrac{v - u}{t}$

weight = mass × gravitational field strength $W = m\,g$

force = mass × acceleration $F = m\,a$

work done = force × distance   work $= F\,d$

power $= \dfrac{\text{energy transferred}}{\text{time}}$ $P = \dfrac{E}{t}$

potential energy = mass × gravitational field strength × height $E_\text{p} = m\,g\,h$

kinetic energy = ½ mass × velocity² $E_\text{k} = \tfrac{1}{2}m\,v^2$

charge = current × time $Q = I\,t$

electrical energy = current × time × voltage $E = I\,t\,V$

voltage = current × resistance $V = I\,R$ Ohm's Law

power = current × voltage $P = I\,V$

power = current² × resistance $P = I^2\,R$

power $= \dfrac{\text{voltage}^2}{\text{resistance}}$ power $= \dfrac{V^2}{R}$

electrical energy = power × time $E = P\,t$

total resistance (series) $R_\text{total} = R_1 + R_2 + R_3$

total resistance (parallel) $\dfrac{1}{R_\text{total}} = \dfrac{1}{R_1} + \dfrac{1}{R_2} + \dfrac{1}{R_3}$

voltage gain $= \dfrac{\text{voltage out}}{\text{voltage in}}$ voltage gain $= \dfrac{V_\text{out}}{V_\text{in}}$

power gain $= \dfrac{\text{power out}}{\text{power in}}$ power gain $= \dfrac{P_\text{out}}{P_\text{in}}$

$$\% \text{ efficiency } = \frac{\text{energy out}}{\text{energy in}} \times 100$$

Note: the formulae below, although in the Standard Grade course, are not covered by any of the content at Higher and so are only included for completeness.

$$\frac{\text{turns in primary}}{\text{turns in secondary}} = \frac{\text{voltage in primary}}{\text{voltage in secondary}} \qquad \frac{n_p}{n_s} = \frac{V_p}{V_s}$$

$$\text{primary voltage} \times \text{primary current} = \text{secondary voltage} \times \text{secondary current} \qquad V_p \times I_p = V_s \times I_s$$

$$\frac{\text{turns in primary}}{\text{turns in secondary}} = \frac{\text{current in secondary}}{\text{current in primary}} \qquad \frac{n_p}{n_s} = \frac{I_s}{I_p}$$

$$\text{heat energy} = \text{specific heat capacity} \times \text{mass} \times \text{change in temperature} \qquad E_h = c\, m\, \Delta T$$

$$\text{heat energy} = \text{mass} \times \text{specific latent heat} \qquad E_h = m\, l$$

Appendix (ii)—Data Sheet

COMMON PHYSICAL QUANTITIES

Quantity	Symbol	Value	Quantity	Symbol	Value
Speed of light in vacuum	c	$3 \cdot 00 \times 10^8$ m s^{-1}	Speed of sound in air	v	340 m s^{-1}
Charge on electron	e	$-1 \cdot 60 \times 10^{-19}$ C	Mass of electron	m_e	$9 \cdot 11 \times 10^{-31}$ kg
Gravitational acceleration	g	$9 \cdot 8$ m s^{-2}	Mass of neutron	m_n	$1 \cdot 675 \times 10^{-27}$ kg
Planck's constant	h	$6 \cdot 63 \times 10^{-34}$ J s	Mass of proton	m_p	$1 \cdot 673 \times 10^{-27}$ kg

REFRACTIVE INDICES

The refractive indices refer to sodium light of wavelength 589 nm and to substances at a temperature of 273 K.

Substance	Refractive index	Substance	Refractive index
Diamond	2·42	Glycerol	1·47
Glass	1·51	Water	1·33
Ice	1·31	Air	1·00
Perspex	1·49		

SPECTRAL LINES

Element	Wavelength/nm	Colour	Element	Wavelength/nm	Colour
Hydrogen	656	Red	Cadmium	644	Red
	486	Blue–green		509	Green
	434	Blue–violet		480	Blue
	410	Violet	Lasers		
	397	Ultraviolet	Element	Wavelength/nm	Colour
	389	Ultraviolet	Carbon dioxide	9550	Infrared
				10590	Infrared
Sodium	589	Yellow	Helium–neon	633	Red

PROPERTIES OF SELECTED MATERIALS

Substance	Density/ kg m^{-3}	Melting Point/ K	Boiling Point/ K	Specific Heat Capacity/ J kg^{-1} K^{-1}	Specific Latent Heat of Fusion/ J kg^{-1}	Specific Latent Heat of Vaporisation/ J kg^{-1}
Aluminium	$2 \cdot 70 \times 10^3$	933	2623	$9 \cdot 02 \times 10^2$	$3 \cdot 95 \times 10^5$	. . . .
Copper	$8 \cdot 96 \times 10^3$	1357	2853	$3 \cdot 86 \times 10^2$	$2 \cdot 05 \times 10^5$	. . . .
Glass	$2 \cdot 60 \times 10^3$	1400	. . . .	$6 \cdot 70 \times 10^2$	. . . .	. . . .
Ice	$9 \cdot 20 \times 10^2$	273	. . . .	$2 \cdot 10 \times 10^3$	$3 \cdot 34 \times 10^5$	. . . .
Glycerol	$1 \cdot 26 \times 10^3$	291	563	$2 \cdot 43 \times 10^3$	$1 \cdot 81 \times 10^5$	$8 \cdot 30 \times 10^5$
Methanol	$7 \cdot 91 \times 10^2$	175	338	$2 \cdot 52 \times 10^3$	$9 \cdot 9 \times 10^4$	$1 \cdot 12 \times 10^6$
Sea Water	$1 \cdot 02 \times 10^3$	264	377	$3 \cdot 93 \times 10^3$	. . . .	. . . .
Water	$1 \cdot 00 \times 10^3$	273	373	$4 \cdot 19 \times 10^3$	$3 \cdot 34 \times 10^5$	$2 \cdot 26 \times 10^6$
Air	1·29	. . . .	. . . .	. . . .	. . . .	. . . .
Hydrogen	$9 \cdot 0 \times 10^{-2}$	14	20	$1 \cdot 43 \times 10^4$	. . . .	$4 \cdot 50 \times 10^5$
Nitrogen	1·25	63	77	$1 \cdot 04 \times 10^3$	. . . .	$2 \cdot 00 \times 10^5$
Oxygen	1·43	55	90	$9 \cdot 18 \times 10^2$	. . . .	$2 \cdot 40 \times 10^5$

The gas densities refer to a temperature of 273 K and a pressure of $1 \cdot 01 \times 10^5$ Pa.

Appendix (iii)—Answers to TQ's

UNIT 1 Mechanics and Properties of Matter

TQ 1

Total distance travelled $= 10 + 4$ m
$$= 14 \text{ m}.$$

Thus average **speed** $= \dfrac{\text{distance}}{\text{time}}$

$$= \dfrac{14}{24}$$

$$= 0.58 \text{ m s}^{-1}$$

Total displacement $= 10$ m due east followed by 4 m due west giving a displacement of 6 m.

average **velocity** $= \dfrac{\text{displacement}}{\text{time}}$

$$= \dfrac{6}{24}$$

$$= 0.25 \text{ m s}^{-1} \text{ due east}$$

TQ 2

acceleration $=$ gradient of graph

$$a = \dfrac{\Delta y}{\Delta x}$$

$$a = \dfrac{-3 - 6}{6}$$

$$a = \dfrac{-9}{6}$$

$$a = -1.5 \text{ m s}^{-2}$$

displacement $=$ area under graph
$$s = (\tfrac{1}{2} \times 4 \times 6) + (\tfrac{1}{2} \times 2 \times -3)$$
$$s = 12 - 3$$
$$s = 9 \text{ m forwards}$$

TQ 3

$$s = ut + \tfrac{1}{2}at^2$$
$$20 = 0 \times t + \tfrac{1}{2} \times 8 \times t^2$$
$$20 = 4t^2$$
$$t^2 = \dfrac{20}{4}$$
$$t = 2.2 \text{ s}$$

TQ 4

(i)
$$v_h = v \cos \theta$$
$$v_h = 12 \cos 30°$$
$$v_h = 10.4 \text{ m s}^{-1}$$

$$v_v = v \sin \theta$$
$$v_v = 12 \sin 30°$$
$$v_v = 6 \text{ m s}^{-1}$$

(ii)
$$v^2 = u^2 + 2as$$
$$0^2 = 6^2 + 2 \times -9.8 \times s$$
$$-36 = -19.6 s$$
$$s = 1.8 \text{ m}$$

(iii) Find time in air during flight from vertical component.
$$v = u + at$$
$$-6 = 6 + -9.8 t$$
$$-12 = -9.8 t$$
$$t = 1.2 \text{ s}$$

then
$$v = \dfrac{s}{t}$$

$$10.4 = \dfrac{s}{1.2}$$

$$s = 12.5 \text{ m}$$

TQ 5

$$F_{un} = ma$$
$$F_{un} = 400 \times 2$$
$$F_{un} = 800 \text{ N}$$

but tension in tow-bar must also overcome 4000 N friction.

$\therefore$ total tension $= 4800$ N

TQ 6

Solution can be found using trigonometry.

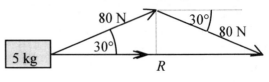

$$r = 2 \times F \cos \theta$$
$$R = 2 \times 80 \cos 30°$$
$$R = 139 \text{ N}$$

$$F_{un} = ma$$
$$139 = 5 \times a$$
$$a = 28 \text{ m s}^{-2}$$

TQ 7
(a) $W = m\,g$

$W = 60 \times 9{\cdot}8$

$W = 588$ N

(b) $F_{un} = m\,a$

$F_{un} = 60 \times 2$

$F_{un} = 120$ N

To produce an unbalanced force downwards of 120 N the scales must push up with a force of 468 N. Thus scales will read 468 N.

TQ 8
(a) $F_{parallel} = m\,g\,\sin\theta$

$F_{parallel} = 2 \times 9{\cdot}8 \times \sin 10°$

$F_{parallel} = 3{\cdot}4$ N

(b) Forces acting down slope $= 1{\cdot}6 + 3{\cdot}4$ N

Forces acting against the motion $= 2$ N

$F_{un} = 3$ N

$F_{un} = m\,a$

$3 = 2 \times a$

$a = 1{\cdot}5$ m s^{-2} down slope.

TQ 9
total momentum before = total momentum after

$(m_A\,u_A) + (m_B\,u_B) = (m_A + m_B)\,v$

$(1{\cdot}5 \times 4) + (2 \times 0) = (1{\cdot}5 + 2)\,v$

$6 + 0 = 3{\cdot}5\,v$

$v = 1{\cdot}71$ m s^{-1}

TQ 10
total momentum before = total momentum after

$(m_A\,u_A) + (m_B\,u_B) = (m_A\,v_A) + (m_B\,v_B)$

$(0{\cdot}1 \times 5) + (0{\cdot}4 \times 0) = (0{\cdot}1 \times 0) + (0{\cdot}4 \times v_B)$

(note: v_A is zero as coconut has no horizontal velocity.)

$0{\cdot}5 + 0 = 0 + 0{\cdot}4\,v_B$

$v_B = \dfrac{0{\cdot}5}{0{\cdot}4}$

$v_B = 1{\cdot}25$ m s^{-1}

TQ 11
total momentum before = total momentum after

$(m_A\,u_A) + (m_B\,u_B) = (m_A\,v_A) + (m_B\,v_B)$

$(60 \times 0) + (1{\cdot}5 \times 0) = (60 \times v_A) + (1{\cdot}5 \times 8)$

$0 + 0 = 60\,v_A + 12$

$60\,v_A = -12$

$v_A = \dfrac{-12}{60}$

$v_A = -0{\cdot}2$ m s^{-1}

TQ 12
$F \times t = \Delta(m\,v)$

$30 \times 0{\cdot}3 = 0{\cdot}4\,v$

$9 = 0{\cdot}4\,v$

$v = 22{\cdot}5$ m s^{-1}

TQ 13
(i) Impulse = area under graph

$= (0{\cdot}5 \times 3 \times 0{\cdot}05) +$

$(0{\cdot}5 \times 3 \times 0{\cdot}15)$

$= 0{\cdot}075 + 0{\cdot}225$

$= 0{\cdot}3$ kg m s^{-1}

(ii) Change in momentum is equivalent to the impulse $= 0{\cdot}3$ kg m s^{-1}

(iii) $\Delta(m\,v) = 0{\cdot}3$ kg m s^{-1}

$0{\cdot}1 \times v = 0{\cdot}3$

$v = \dfrac{0{\cdot}3}{0{\cdot}1}$

$v = 3$ m s^{-1}

TQ 14
$\varrho = \dfrac{m}{V}$

$1\,190 = \dfrac{m}{0{\cdot}02}$

$m = 1\,190 \times 0{\cdot}02$

$m = 23{\cdot}8$ kg

TQ 15
$p = \dfrac{F}{A}$

$10\,000 = \dfrac{F}{1{\cdot}5 \times 10^{-3}}$

$F = 15$ N

TQ 16
$p = \rho\,g\,h$

$p = 1{\cdot}00 \times 10^{3} \times 10 \times 5$

$p = 5{\cdot}0 \times 10^{4}$ Pa

total pressure $= 1{\cdot}0 \times 10^{5} + 5{\cdot}0 \times 10^{4}$

$= 1{\cdot}5 \times 10^{5}$ Pa

TQ 17

(a) weight of balloon $= m\,g$
$$= 0.015 \times 9.8$$
$$= 0.147 \text{ N}$$
upward force $=$ buoyancy force $-$ weight
$$= 0.177 - 0.0.147$$
$$= 0.03 \text{ N}$$

(b) $F_{un} = m\,a$
$$0.03 = 0.015 \times a$$
$$a = \frac{0.03}{0.015}$$
$$a = 2 \text{ m s}^{-2}$$

TQ 18

$$p_1 V_1 = p_2 V_2$$
$$100 \times 2.5 = 40 \times V_2$$
$$V_2 = \frac{100 \times 2.5}{40}$$
$$V_2 = 6.25 \text{ m}^3$$

TQ 19

$$\frac{p_1}{T_1} = \frac{p_2}{T_2}$$
$$\frac{6 \times 10^5}{300} = \frac{p_2}{220}$$
$$300\,p_2 = 6 \times 10^5 \times 220$$
$$p_2 = 4.4 \times 10^5 \text{ Pa}$$

TQ 20

$$\frac{p_1 V_1}{T_1} = \frac{p_2 V_2}{T_2}$$
$$\frac{1 \times 10^5 \times 4}{300} = \frac{0.6 \times 10^5 \times V_2}{250}$$
cross multiply
$$1.8 \times 10^7\, V_2 = 1 \times 10^8$$
$$V_2 = 5.56 \text{ m}^3$$

UNIT 2 Electricity and Electronics

TQ 21

work done on electron $=$ gain in kinetic energy
$$Q\,V = \tfrac{1}{2} m\, v^2$$
$$1.60 \times 10^{-19} \times 4\,000 = \tfrac{1}{2} \times 9.11 \times 10^{-31} \times v^2$$
$$v^2 = \frac{1.60 \times 10^{-19} \times 4\,000}{\tfrac{1}{2} \times 9.11 \times 10^{-31}}$$
$$v^2 = 1.4 \times 10^{15}$$
$$v = 3.7 \times 10^7 \text{ m s}^{-1}$$

The negative sign on the electron charge can be ignored in the calculation.—it is negative because an electron has negative charge.

TQ 22

(a) Reading will be 3 V as there is no current flowing so the voltage across the cell will be equal to the e.m.f.

(b) E.m.f. $= I(R + r)$
$$3 = I(11 + 1)$$
$$I = \frac{3}{12}$$
$$I = 0.25 \text{ A}$$

(c) Voltage across cell $=$ t.p.d. when switch is closed
$$\text{t.p.d.} = I\,R$$
$$\text{t.p.d.} = 0.25 \times 11$$
$$\text{t.p.d.} = 2.75 \text{ V}$$

(d) 'lost volts' $= I\,r$
'lost volts' $= 0.25 \times 1$
'lost volts' $= 0.25 \text{ V}$

TQ 23

e.m.f. $=$ intercept on voltage axis
e.m.f. $= 0.44 \text{ V}$

$-r =$ gradient of graph
$$-r = \frac{y_2 - y_1}{x_2 - x_1}$$
$$-r = \frac{0.44 - 0.24}{0 - 0.040}$$
$$-r = \frac{0.20}{-0.04}$$
$$-r = -5\ \Omega$$

Internal resistance of cell $= 5\ \Omega$

TQ 24

Total resistance of 50 Ω bulb and 100 Ω resistor in parallel is33.3 Ω

Voltage across section of potentiometer is
$$\frac{33}{133} \times 12 = 3 \text{ V}$$

TQ 25

$$\frac{R_1}{R_2} = \frac{R_3}{R_X}$$

$$\frac{40}{500} = \frac{160}{R_X}$$

$$R_X = \frac{500 \times 160}{40}$$

$$R_X = 2\ 000\ \Omega$$

TQ 26

(a)

$$V_{rms} = \frac{V_{peak}}{\sqrt{2}}$$

$$V_{rms} = \frac{16}{\sqrt{2}}$$

$$V_{rms} = 11 \cdot 3\ V$$

(b)

$$I_{peak} = \frac{V_{peak}}{R} \qquad I_{rms} = \frac{V_{rms}}{R}$$

$$I_{peak} = \frac{16}{30} \qquad I_{rms} = \frac{11 \cdot 3}{30}$$

$$I_{peak} = 0 \cdot 53\ A \qquad I_{rms} = 0 \cdot 38\ A$$

TQ 27

$$C = \frac{Q}{V}$$

$$2200 \times 10^{-6} = \frac{Q}{12}$$

$$Q = 2 \cdot 6 \times 10^{-2}\ C$$

TQ 28

(a)

$$E = \tfrac{1}{2} C V^2$$

$$400 \times 10^{-3} = \tfrac{1}{2} \times 1000 \times 10^{-6}\ V^2$$

$$V^2 = \frac{400 \times 10^{-3}}{500 \times 10^{-6}}$$

$$V^2 = 800\ V$$

$$V = 28 \cdot 3\ V$$

(b)

$$Q = C V$$

$$Q = 1000 \times 10^{-6} \times 28 \cdot 3$$

$$Q = 0 \cdot 0283\ C$$

TQ 29

(a)

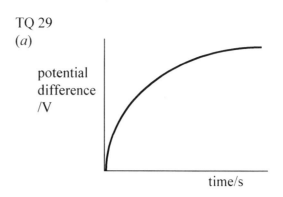

potential difference /V

time/s

(b)

$$V = IR$$

$$1 \cdot 5 = I \times 1000$$

$$I = 1 \cdot 5\ mA$$

(c)

$$E = \tfrac{1}{2} C V^2$$

$$E = \tfrac{1}{2} \times 2200 \times 10^{-6} \times 1 \cdot 5^2$$

$$E = 2 \cdot 48 \times 10^{-3}\ J$$

TQ 30

$$\frac{V_o}{V_1} = -\frac{R_f}{R_1}$$

$$\frac{V_o}{100 \times 10^{-3}} = -\frac{5000}{500}$$

$$500\ V_o = -5000 \times 100 \times 10^{-3}$$

$$V_o = -1\ V$$

TQ 31

(a) Differential mode.

(b) $$V_o = (V_2 - V_1)\frac{R_f}{R_1}$$

$$V_o = (1 \cdot 8 - 1 \cdot 5)\frac{50\ 000}{2000}$$

$$V_o = 0 \cdot 3 \times 25$$

$$V_o = 7 \cdot 5\ V$$

UNIT 3 Radiation and Matter

TQ 32

$$T = \frac{1}{f}$$

$$T = \frac{1}{500}$$

$$T = 2 \times 10^{-3} \text{ s}$$

TQ 33

Path difference $= 85 - 65 = 20$ cm.

$\frac{20}{10} = 2\lambda$ so producing constructive interference.

TQ 34

(i) moving the reflector back 1 cm introduces a path difference of 2 cm which is ½ λ. This gives destructive interference.

(ii) moving the reflector back 2 cm introduces a path difference of 4 cm which is 1 λ. This gives constructive interference.

(iii) moving the reflector back 4 cm introduces a path difference of 8 cm which is 2 λ. This gives constructive interference.

TQ 35

$$d = \frac{1}{\text{number of lines per metre}}$$

$$d = \frac{1}{100\,000}$$

$$d = 1 \times 10^{-5}$$

$$n\lambda = d\sin\theta$$

$$1 \times \lambda = 1 \times 10^{-5} \sin 4 \cdot 0^{\circ}$$

$$\lambda = 6 \cdot 98 \times 10^{-7} \text{ m}$$

$$\text{or } 698 \text{ nm}$$

This wavelength represents light at the red end of the spectrum.

TQ 36

$$n = \frac{\sin \theta_{air}}{\sin \theta_{glass}}$$

$$n = \frac{\sin 30^{\circ}}{\sin 19^{\circ}}$$

$$n = 1 \cdot 54$$

TQ 37

$$n = \frac{v_{air}}{v_{glass}}$$

$$n = \frac{3 \times 10^8}{2 \times 10^8}$$

$$n = 1 \cdot 5$$

$$n = \frac{\lambda_{air}}{\lambda_{glass}}$$

$$1 \cdot 5 = \frac{600 \times 10^{-9}}{\lambda_{glass}}$$

$$\lambda_{glass} = 400 \times 10^{-9} \text{ m}$$

TQ 38

$$n = \frac{\sin \theta_{air}}{\sin \theta_{glass}}$$

$$n = \frac{\sin 65^{\circ}}{\sin 40^{\circ}}$$

$$n = 1 \cdot 4$$

Find the critical angle.

$$n = \frac{1}{\sin C}$$

$$1 \cdot 4 = \frac{1}{\sin C}$$

$$\sin C = \frac{1}{1 \cdot 4}$$

$$C = 45 \cdot 6^{\circ}$$

Light strikes the glass surface at X above the critical angle so is totally internally reflected.

TQ 39

$$I = \frac{P}{\text{area}}$$

$$I = \frac{300}{2 \times 1 \cdot 5}$$

$$I = 100 \text{ W m}^{-2}$$

TQ 40

$$I_1 d_1^2 = I_2 d_2^2$$

$$10 \times 0 \cdot 8^2 = I_2 \times 2^2$$

$$I_2 = \frac{6 \cdot 4}{4}$$

$$I_2 = 1 \cdot 6 \text{ W m}^{-2}$$

TQ 41

$$E = hf$$
$$E = 6{\cdot}63 \times 10^{-34} \times 8{\cdot}4 \times 10^{14}$$
$$E = 5{\cdot}6 \times 10^{-19} \text{ J}$$

This is less than the work function so no electrons will be ejected.

TQ 42

$$I = Nhf$$
$$8 = N \times 6{\cdot}63 \times 10^{-34} \times 5 \times 10^{14}$$
$$N = 2{\cdot}4 \times 10^{19} \text{ electrons}$$

TQ 43

$$E_2 - E_1 = hf$$
$$-15{\cdot}83 \times 10^{-19} - -3{\cdot}40 \times 10^{-19} = 6{\cdot}63 \times 10^{-34} \times f$$
$$f = 1{\cdot}87 \times 10^{15}$$

$$v = f\lambda$$
$$3 \times 10^8 = 1{\cdot}87 \times 10^{15} \times \lambda$$
$$\lambda = 1{\cdot}6 \times 10^{-7} \text{ m (1600 nm)}$$

TQ 44

$$^{226}_{88}\text{Ra} + {}^4_2\text{He} + {}^4_2\text{He} + {}^0_{-1}\text{e} \rightarrow {}^{234}_{91}\text{Pa}$$

i.e. 2 α and 1 β.

TQ 45

(a) Fusion.

(b)

LHS	RHS
$3{\cdot}342 \times 10^{-27}$	$5{\cdot}005 \times 10^{-27}$
$3{\cdot}342 \times 10^{-27}$	$1{\cdot}675 \times 10^{-27}$
$6{\cdot}684 \times 10^{-27}$	$6{\cdot}680 \times 10^{-27}$

$$\text{mass change} = 6{\cdot}684 \times 10^{-27} - 6{\cdot}680 \times 10^{-27}$$
$$= 0{\cdot}4 \times 10^{-29} \text{ kg}$$

$$E = mc^2$$
$$E = 0{\cdot}4 \times 10^{-29} \times (3 \times 10^8)^2$$
$$E = 3{\cdot}6 \times 10^{-13} \text{ J}$$

TQ 46

$$A = \frac{N}{t}$$
$$2 \times 10^6 = \frac{N}{60}$$
$$N = 1{\cdot}2 \times 10^8 \text{ decays}$$

TQ 47

(a)
$$H = DQ$$
$$H = 20 \times 10^{-6} \times 1$$
$$H = 20 \times 10^{-6} \text{ Sv}$$

(b)
$$\dot{H} = \frac{H}{t}$$
$$\dot{H} = \frac{20 \times 10^{-6}}{40}$$
$$\dot{H} = 5 \times 10^{-7} \text{ Sv h}^{-1}$$

TQ 48

(a) 4000 μSv → 2000μSv → 1000μSv → 500μSv → 250μSv → 125μSv
5 half thickness'.
$\therefore$ total thickness $= 5 \times 1{\cdot}2$
$$= 6 \text{ cm.}$$

(b) Radiation obeys the inverse square law so increasing the distance between the source and the body greatly decreases the absorbed dose.

Uncertainties

TQ 49

(a)
$$\text{mean} = \frac{\text{sum of all measurements}}{\text{number of measurements}}$$
$$\text{mean} = \frac{80{\cdot}8 + 81{\cdot}0 + 80{\cdot}3 + 80{\cdot}9 + 81{\cdot}2}{5}$$
$$\text{mean} = 80{\cdot}8°\text{C}$$

(b)
$$\text{random uncertainty} = \frac{\text{max. reading} - \text{min. reading}}{\text{number of readings}}$$
$$\text{random uncertainty} = \frac{81{\cdot}2 - 80{\cdot}3}{5}$$
$$\text{random uncertainty} = \pm 0{\cdot}18°\text{C}$$

TQ 50

(a)
length of vehicle:
$$\text{uncertainty} = \frac{0{\cdot}5}{150} \times \frac{100}{1}$$
$$\text{uncertainty} = \pm 0{\cdot}33\%$$

time:
$$\text{uncertainty} = \frac{0{\cdot}01}{0{\cdot}2} \times \frac{100}{1}$$
$$\text{uncertainty} = \pm 5\%$$

TQ 50 (continued)

(b)

$$v = \frac{s}{t}$$

$$v = \frac{0 \cdot 150}{0 \cdot 2}$$

$$v = 0 \cdot 75 \text{ m s}^{-1}$$

% uncertainty taken as $\pm 5\%$

$$\text{absolute uncertainty} = 0 \cdot 75 \times \frac{5}{100}$$

$$\text{absolute uncertainty} = 0 \cdot 038 \text{ m s}^{-1}$$

$$\text{speed} = 0 \cdot 75 \text{ m s}^{-1} \pm 0 \cdot 04 \text{ m s}^{-1}$$